Becoming the Greatest Expression of You

Create Your Future to be Greater than Your Past

Roger Moore
GreatestExpressionBook.com

Becoming the Greatest Expression of You: Create Your Future to be Greater than Your Past

Roger Moore

Published in the United States of America by Maluhia Publishing

ISBN: 978-1-7356433-0-4

Library of Congress Control Number: 2021917069

First Printing: September 2021

Portions of this book were originally published as blog posts at HypnosisHealthInfo.com

Roger Moore
Medical Hypnotherapist
69525 Dillon Road #138
Desert Hot Springs, CA 92241

(760) 219-8079

www.RogerMooreBooks.com
www. GreatestExpressionBook.com

Roger Moore is available to speak at your group, business, or conference event on a variety of topics. Call (760) 219-8079 for booking information.

What You Could Gain from Reading This Book

If you're like most people, you live your life based on past experiences. Rather than using the past as a source of wisdom to live fully in the present, you allow your past to be a script to live by. Your old story limits your abundant possibilities to live more wholly in the moment and create a better future. In this book, you'll learn how to write a new story for your life, so you can invent your future to be greater than your past.

Beloved doctor and writer, Bernie S. Siegel, MD, has written: "My own day-to-day clinical experience has convinced me the state of the mind changes the state of the body by working through the central nervous system, the endocrine system, and the immune system. . . . Peace of mind sends the body a 'live' message. Thus, all healing is scientific even if science can't yet explain exactly how the unexpected 'miracles' occur."

Becoming the Greatest Expression of You reveals the most effective methods for sending those live messages to your body, so you, too, can receive unexpected miracles.

Are you ready to make lasting change? Do you want these changes to feel significant and meaningful?

The methods in this book were developed over twenty-five years with hundreds of my clients who have physically, mentally, emotionally, and spiritually improved their lives. If you're ready to make lasting and meaningful changes, then this is the book for you.

Written by a Leading Expert with Fifty Years' Experience

Roger Moore is a Professional Medical Hypnotherapist certified by the International Certification Board of Clinical Hypnotherapists (ICBCH) and by the International Medical & Dental Hypnotherapy Association (IMDHA) and an expert in helping people to create their future to be greater than their past. He has a master's degree in Marriage Family Therapy with training and experience in criminal justice, chemical dependency counseling, and is an end-of-life doula.

Roger knows personally about creating lasting change. In 1996, he released over 120 pounds and has kept it off ever since and has helped hundreds of others to let go of weight and keep it off with his Slender For Life™ weight loss hypnosis program.

Roger is known as the therapist's therapist and is the go-to guy for mental health counselors, clergy, and healthcare specialists throughout the world. He is the recipient of the Lifetime Achievement Award by the IMDHA.

Throughout his career, he has led many cancer support groups, was a team member at the Peninsula Cancer Center in Poulsbo, WA., and is an active participant in the Parkinson's Resource Organization's Wellness Village.

The Roger Moore Institute of Hypnotherapy offers online Medical Hypnosis training for healthcare professionals.

Roger was presented the IMDHA Pen & Quill award for his book, ***Becoming Slender For Life***.

Roger Moore is the Medical Hypnosis expert that is known worldwide for his work with autoimmune diseases, cancer, dementia/Alzheimer's, end-of-life, chronic pain, weight loss, trauma, stress, and anxiety. He teaches self-hypnosis strategies that actually work and how you can do them at home.

Becoming the Greatest Expression of You is explained step-by-step and, when you are finished with this book, you will have easy-to-use and practical resources that you can use for the rest of your life.

Do you want Roger Moore to help you to create your future to be greater than your past?

Call (760) 219-8079 or visit HypnosisHealthInfo.com.

Watch for the new workbook to help put your specific personal goals into action!
GreatestExpressionBook.com

What Others Are Saying About This Book

"*Becoming the Greatest Expression of You* is truly a guidebook to life. The mind is a powerful resource which we all need to understand and use in a constructive and not self-destructive way. Roger's book can guide you and coach you to find your inner talents and potential. Read it, and you will find your path to a healthier and healed life and body. I know from experience what he says is the way." **~Bernie Siegel, MD, author of *Love, Medicine & Miracles* and *No Endings Only Beginnings***

"Making the change is the hardest part of regaining lost health and appearances. I have spent many decades working with Roger Moore in helping patients make serious changes in their diet. Hypnosis, as taught in *Becoming the Greatest Expression of You*, has been found to be a powerful tool for changing behaviors, resulting in eating habits that support health and healing." **~John McDougall, MD, Founder of the McDougall Program, Internist and Educator**

"Roger Moore quickly dives into the shame-based belief so many of us carry throughout our lives, the belief that we are not good enough. The essence of the book empowers the reader with tools to counter that belief allowing you to live in the present and not have your life dominated by a past script. In *Becoming the Greatest Expression of You*, he inspires and teaches us to become our best self—to know joy and hope. Based on his knowledge of neuroscience, he offers a clear path that allows the reader to quickly feel the potential for change. It is an exciting book as you feel his passion, compassion, love, and humbleness to lift us all to a higher plane in life. It's a beautiful book that I will immediately give to both friends, family, and clients." **~Claudia Black, addiction specialist, Author of *It Will Never Happen to Me* and *Unspoken Legacy***

"In his book *Becoming the Greatest Expression of You*, Roger Moore offers us tools, both simple and profound, to finally grow beyond old trauma and limiting beliefs and truly manifest our Best Selves. While we all long to be our best, Roger shows us how to actually become our best through practices he has validated in his years of work as a hypnotherapist. Read this book to find joy, free up your innate ability to love unconditionally, and live each moment of your life as fully as possible." **~Karen Wyatt MD, Author of *7 Lessons for Living from the Dying*; host of End-of-Life University Podcast**

"Roger Moore has created an amazing tool to help anyone create the life they were meant to experience with this step-by-step guide. Having the honor of working with over 1,000 people at the end of life, it is the "regrets" that cause people the most pain at this last period of time. Life is challenging, but with the tools in this book, we can all be able to access the best journey possible." **~Suzanne B. O'Brien RN, Founder and CEO International Doulagivers Institute**

"Read this book to truly reward yourself with a goldmine of healthy living advice. Roger is a genuine expert with loads of real-life experiences that are put to use brilliantly in this book. People from all walks of life will gain insight on how to use this unique mindful skill set. I will be recommending this gem to my patients as well as family and friends." **~P. Jeff Smith, DO, board-certified physiatrist, interventional sports, spine, and precision pain management physician, Eisenhower Desert Orthopedic Center.**

"Tired of repeating your past? Roger Moore's latest book clearly presents how you can create lasting change so that your future can be greater than your past. Using these simple and powerful techniques, thousands of people have improved their physical, mental, emotional, and spiritual wellness. You too can use the power of your mind and achieve extraordinary results and create your own destiny!" **~Patrick Snow, Publishing Coach and International Best-Selling Author of *Creating Your Own Destiny, The Affluent Entrepreneur*, and *Boy Entrepreneur***

"I had the pleasure of working with Roger Moore for several years at Peninsula Cancer Center, where he led a support group of patients. As an experienced cancer doctor, I know that a diagnosis of cancer can be a wake-up call that we are, in fact, mortal, and life can be short. It is often a time of self-reflection and re-evaluation of our relationships and goals. If we are not living an authentic version of ourselves, it is a great time to make changes and live well. Roger Moore has written a very readable and relatable guide to making significant and meaningful changes to one's life. He illustrates his book with interesting and compelling stories from his practice and an easy-to-understand pathway to becoming the greatest expression of you." **~Berit L. Madsen, MD, FACR, board-certified radiation oncologist**

"Over the last decade, I have had the opportunity to refer numerous patients to Dr. Moore, and there is no question that they have benefited immensely from his expertise in the domain of medical hypnotherapy. From the challenging and ubiquitous problems of tobacco cessation, insomnia, and weight loss to the often overwhelming crises of cancer and terminal diagnoses, Roger has given effective and compassionate tools to my patients again and again. The skills he teaches empower courage, equanimity, and perseverance in the face of life's intractable obstacles. His work is a valuable adjunct to modern medicine, which often flounders in those existential peripheries Roger so wonderfully illuminates. I consider him a vital and trusted partner in the care of my patients." **~Dr. Mark McCabe, MD, internal medicine, Seattle, WA**

My Gratitude

Thank you to the many people and our dog Luna who made this book possible;

My wife Marilyn: You patiently read each chapter two, three and four times, editing and proofreading. Thank you, my love, for your love, support, and encouragement.

My son Josh: I admire the man that you have become and thank you for helping me to be a better me.

My stepchildren: Larry, always remember you are a healer. **Shellee**, your heart radiates love. **Tim**, thank you for your love.

My ten granddaughters: You spark my JOY!

September Herrin and Kelley T. Woods: your editing, comments, guidance, and friendship is valued beyond measure.

Dr. Richard Nongard: without your friendship, collegiality, and teaching, this book would still be a series of 131 blog posts.

Oriana Green: you have encouraged, guided, nudged, pushed, admonished and looked out for me for the past fifteen years. Your love, friendship, editing, direction, art, and internet skills have been a mainstay.

To all of the clients over the past twenty-five years: you have been my teachers, and I have received so much from you. I look forward to each session with you with anticipation and curiosity to discover what opportunities for learning you will present to me.

Luna: you were our heart dog, and your unconditional love is a paw print on my heart forever.

Testimonial

Hello Roger!

It has been quite some time since our last session together. I wanted to take a moment to check in with you and let you know how important and impactful your program has been for me. My life is transformed.

I used the tools taught to me in our sessions, as well as the *Becoming Slender* For *Life* book and MP3s, and more recently, The Greatest Expression of You website blog posts. Not only was I able to release the excess weight (which was my original goal), but I was able to uncover painful and misleading "truths" which caused me to carry excess weight and act in a manner which promoted this.

My behavior has changed because my thoughts about myself have changed. For the first time in my entire life, I love and respect myself. I found the root of the problem and made peace with it, forgiving myself for judging myself and others. Growing up in the shadow of my beautiful and talented ballerina sister left me feeling stale and ugly, certainly not worthy of the love and affection of my parents. After-school snacks and seconds at the dinner table were comfortable to me. The use of food for comfort continued as I entered the workplace in my twenties and manifested in other ways as I got older. I was never NOT on a diet—restricting carbohydrates, calories, or gluten. I was vegan, pescatarian, intermittent fasting, juice-detoxing, and starving myself. There was no consistency or balance and no act of self-love.

Thanks to your kind words and your amazing program, I am a new person. I never knew my "ideal" weight was different from my goal weight. Once I changed my behavior patterns, the weight easily and effortlessly slipped away and with it my invisible armor. I am no longer afraid of being vulnerable or expressing love to others. And for the first time since childhood, I love my body and myself.

Thank you, thank you, thank you for your incredible, life-transforming program! You are intelligent to have created it with such mastery, and I look forward to your next book.

In gratitude and love,

April,
January 26, 2021

Table of Contents

Foreword by Kelley T. Woods

Imagine that you were able to discover how to create sustainable change in yourself and in your life. In an era where self-help offerings exist in abundance, it is wonderful to find a book that not only contains real substance but provides information that is palatable and easy to apply. In the pages that follow, you will gain confidence in being able to use the power of your mind to create desired positive changes. You may even be surprised at how easy Roger Moore makes this for you!

As a friend and colleague of Roger's for more than a decade, I have had the pleasure to teach with him, to learn from him, and to be able to share my own insights with him. That last part is special: the smartest people in the world are those who know they still have more to learn. You have purchased this book because you are open to learning; your curious mind is eager to find out how you can become the best version of yourself.

Another special aspect about the author of this book is that he walks his talk. This is crucial because not only has Roger successfully used the principles in this book within his decades of client work, but he also uses them in his everyday life. As a fellow hypnosis practitioner, I have the most respect for my colleagues who use hypnosis and mindfulness practices to help themselves!

Helping yourself—this is an interesting concept, isn't it? There was a time of rugged independence in most cultures' history (more recently in my own here in the United States of America) where one took responsibility for their own welfare. This happened not just because of a sense of liberty or self-directed determination but because of not having another choice. People simply moved on because survival forced them to.

With the progression of civilization, personal responsibilities steadily became co-opted by others—schools, employers, governments, etc. Along with this, without even realizing, many people gradually gave away the ability to govern themselves on a personal level. They forgot that they have the power to determine how they are thinking, feeling, and behaving.

This learned dependency has resulted in a diminishing sense of control and a correlating increase in states of depression, anxiety, and related chronic health issues. An underlying theme for many who are suspended in modern culture is a crippling sense of helplessness and hopelessness. Increasing rates of illness, addiction, and suicide reflect this truth.

With this book, Roger plays the role of Master Chef, not only offering you fantastic recipes for taking back control of yourself and your life but also teaching you how to become a skilled chef. Roger invites you to take these recipes, to make them your own, to play with them for your benefit. After reading and practicing what he offers here, you will be able to construct the life that you want using your most powerful asset: your mind.

So, keep your curious mind open as you enter this fascinating realm. Allow yourself to imagine what marvelous results you will soon achieve from this blessing of a book by Roger Moore.

Kelley T. Woods

Practitioner of Hypnosis

Anacortes, Washington

Chapter 1

Your Best Self

"God, help me be the guy that Luna thinks I am."
—Roger Moore

If you could be **Your Best Self**, who would you be? Not what you would do, but who would you be? By *who,* I don't mean to suggest you think of another person such as a hero, but rather who you are at your core. If you are being **Your Best Self**, who are you?

Do you believe that it's even possible to be **Your Best Self**?

Take a moment right now and close your eyelids. Go within yourself. What are the qualities that those who know you, love you, and look up to you see in you? Maybe they see that you are loving, kind, and fun. Perhaps they see you as joyous, compassionate, or gracious.

I've come close to accepting that when I ask people to tell me about their best self, they will tell me about what they do. It's rare for someone to start telling me about who they are and what's in their heart. Focusing on *doing* reminds me of what the

Apostle, Paul, wrote in Romans 11:6 about salvation by good deeds rather than what is in our hearts. He said that if salvation is by grace, then it's not about works. If salvation is by works, then it is no longer a gift but rather a reward for what we do. I like to think that the Greatest Expression of You is an acknowledgement of the gifts within you. These are the gifts that you have to share with the world. The gifts that you bring to this party called Life. These gifts are gifts of grace that make up your Beingness.

My client caseload is filled with people who feel inadequate to do enough. The problem with *doing*, as I see it, is that trying to overcome anger, hurt, fear, and sadness, by doing things leads to stress and anxiety, and often to hopelessness and despair.

When we are wrapped up in the performances of doing, we recognize that others are doing more or better than we are. Even when we are doing great things, 70 percent of us experience the imposter syndrome, haunted by limiting thoughts:

"What if they find out that I'm faking it? What if I get busted?"

The actions of doing can quickly and easily lead to thoughts of inadequacy, of not being good enough, being less than, and a host of other judgments that beat you down. These judgments can easily result in depression, anxiety, loneliness, and despair.

For more than thirteen years, my wife and I have loved a white lab named Luna. Each morning as I brush my teeth, I meditate on this phrase, "God, help me be the person that Luna thinks I am." In Luna's eyes, I can do no wrong. Sure, she may jump up if I sneeze too loud or give me the stink eye when I give her medicine she does not like. But immediately after, she starts to wag her tail and flops onto the floor to cuddle with me, wanting a belly rub. As soon as I walk through the door when I return home, she comes to me with her tail wagging, butt wiggling, and a big smile. The look in her eyes is one of unconditional love and acceptance.

I strive to be the person Luna thinks I am. When I recognize that I am crabby and stressed, I check in and ask, "Am I being who Luna thinks I am?" This question is enough of a reminder to help me shift into being the best me that I can be in that moment.

Being **My Best Self** is about ending the emphasis on doing and rediscovering the joy of being your best self in this moment. Being **My Best Self** is about stopping self-judgments of inadequacy and disparaging emotions that we try to mask with food, alcohol, cigarettes, drugs, spending, sexual addiction, pornography, and a host of other destructive behaviors.

Throughout the first two-thirds of my life, food was my drug of choice to numb out painful emotions. How about you? What painful thoughts and emotions do you try to avoid? What destructive behaviors do you use to distract yourself?

Unfortunately, these unhelpful thoughts and emotions can become addictive and keep you stuck in the same patterns of behavior. Studies in neuroscience have demonstrated that these negative thoughts and emotions are addictive and can become hardwired. Your body is hardwired to respond to stress in ways that are meant to protect you against threats from dangerous situations. When you are stressed by real or perceived events, your hypothalamus sets off an alarm system in your body, causing the release of adrenaline and cortisol. Your body becomes addicted to these chemicals created by anger, hurt, fear, and sadness, and when you try to change these thoughts of anger, hurt, fear, and sadness, you experience a physical withdrawal like you would from a drug. Your body becomes accustomed to suffering and misery. These states may feel familiar, perhaps even safe. It is what you know. Changing your thoughts and your emotions can create a whole new set of stress and anxiety.

I don't know about your experience, but for me, Not Good Enough is a message that I had believed for as long as I can remember. In fact, this limiting belief ran my life. I tried time and time again to change this belief and overcome its influence on my life but thinking differently felt so uncomfortable and unfamiliar that I couldn't maintain thoughts and beliefs affirming that I am enough.

Not Good Enough had become part of my personality. It had become automatic and familiar. As miserable as believing I wasn't good enough made me feel, this belief was comfortable. No matter how much I did or how hard I tried, it was never enough.

There was a key moment in my life that helped anchor my belief that I was not good enough. When I was eight years old, my dad sold his 160-acre farm—including cows, pigs, chickens, lambs, and my horse. We left the big farmhouse and the wide-open spaces of southern Minnesota for a small apartment above a motel my father bought in Iowa. I did not want to move. My dad explained to me that my brother, who was seventeen years old, did not want to farm and was moving to San Diego after graduation. Since I couldn't do the work my brother did, and my dad didn't want to do all the work himself, the farm had to be sold.

What I heard was a message that I wasn't good enough, I wasn't capable, and it was my fault we had to sell the farm. For many years, Not Good Enough ran my life. For far too many years, I lived my life with this perception. I accepted evidence that I was not good enough and added it as proof to support my perception.

Many years later, at a family reunion, one of my uncles asked my dad why he sold the farm. He replied that my brother didn't want to farm and that I was only eight years old at the time. An eight-year-old could not do the work of a seventeen-year-old, and at the age of forty-five, my dad didn't want to do all the hard work himself. In that moment, it was as if a veil was lifted from me. For the first time, I understood the reality that my dad could not do all the work himself and that reality wasn't about me. The story I made up and lived by just was not true.

The emotional hit I took by thinking that my dad was telling me I'm not good enough hardwired those neurons together. For the next thirty years, I had lived my life with that belief. Not Good Enough became part of my personality. Every time those neurons fired, I got an addictive hit of the chemical release from those neurons.

Intellectually, I could tell myself this belief wasn't true. But, and here's the rub, when I tried to willpower my way to being good enough, my body went into chemical withdrawal because those neurons weren't firing.

The withdrawal that my body experienced soon brought me back to my familiar, comfortable belief that kept me from moving forward with my goals.

These invisible barriers and boundaries are created and maintained in your unconscious mind. You trap yourself, stuck in your tracks by a thought, by the feeling that some places are off-limits, that where you are is safe if you stay put, satisfied to be where you are.

To my eight-year-old mind, the idea that I'm not good enough helped me make sense of my dad selling this farm that I so dearly loved. In fact, I would suggest that this decision was a demonstration of my resilience. It helped me to move through my grief and sadness of leaving a large farmhouse that I loved and the many animals there that had become my pets to live in a small apartment above a motel. This belief helped me wrap my head around such a drastic change of lifestyle.

Not only did I accept Not Good Enough as a belief, but sadness, grief, and loss were hardwired as well. Sadness felt normal, whereas the emotions of happiness, silliness, and jubilance felt uncomfortable and even abnormal.

The problem, of course, is that a decision made and the emotions developed by an eight-year-old didn't serve me well when I was fifteen, thirty, sixty, or at this moment in time. Fortunately, Not Good Enough no longer runs my life. The thought still shows up, but I now have a different relationship with it.

We assign meaning to the events in life. I decided that moving from the farm to town was a terrible thing, and I suffered for many years as a result of this choice. I realize now that I could have just as easily chosen to be happy at the prospects of living close to new friends, the town swimming pool, and riding my bike on paved streets.

Since 1997, I have been in private practice as a Medical Hypnotherapist and marriage and family therapist. I recognize a common theme in the hundreds of people who have come through my doors.

I've observed that most of these people were living some aspect of their life based upon events of the past that resulted in emotions that no longer serve them and self-limiting decisions they had made long ago. The meanings that they assigned to these events caused pain and suffering physically, mentally, emotionally, and spiritually.

Think about it for a moment: Where in your life do old emotions (anger, hurt, fear, sadness) and limiting beliefs and decisions hold you back today?

So, what are the meanings that you have assigned to the events in your life? What has been the resulting self-talk? How have these messages run your life? What pain and suffering have you experienced as a result of the meaning you gave to these events? How are these messages holding you back from being your best self? What if you were to give these events a new meaning? How would your life be different if you changed your relationship with these messages?

One of my favorite stories as a small boy was *Peter and the Wolf*. Over the years, I've had the opportunity to read this story to my granddaughters on several occasions, and I very much enjoyed the experience. (Truthfully, it was more about getting time with a granddaughter than it was about the story.) As much as I like *Peter and the Wolf*, imagine if I read that same story several times a day, every day from the time I learned to read until now. Imagine telling yourself the same story over and over and over and over again.

That sounds boring, anxiety-ridden, and depressing. I imagine at some point becoming angry from hearing the story again and again and again and again!

What stories are you telling yourself over and over and over and over again? What emotions are your go-to emotions?

These old stories and their accompanying emotions can hold you back from achieving most any goal.

Recognizing and changing the meanings we hold on to can be challenging. For several years my wife and I vacationed on Salt Spring Island. It's one of the Gulf Islands in the Salish Sea between mainland British Columbia, Canada, and Vancouver Island. Deer freely roam this rural island leaving well-worn trails that seemed to be perfect for hiking the hills and mountain slopes. In some places, rain rushed down these trails, and these paths became deep ruts that were difficult to climb out of or even to walk in. That's how it is with the stories we tell ourselves. The meanings we give to events, the emotions we hold on to become so deeply rutted that they neurologically hardwire. One of the great things about being human is that we can change and climb out of our old ruts. Read on, and I will show you how to rewire neurology and get out of the old mental, emotional, and physical ruts and create a future that is better than your past.

In 1998, I met Sylvia, a delightful woman who was then in her late seventies. Having been overweight since the birth of her first child, Sylvia had sixty pounds she wanted to let go of. In one of our sessions, I asked her if it was okay for her to release her extra weight or did she need to keep those extra pounds. She looked stunned but only hesitated for a moment before telling me about how she loved her husband of over forty years and had a monogamous relationship with him. She also explained that she'd been sexually promiscuous as a young adult, prior to meeting her husband. Sylvia realized she feared that if she were at her ideal weight, she would again be attractive to other men and cheat on her husband. I asked her if she was the same person today as she was in her twenties, and if she were presented with the opportunity now, would she really cheat on her husband.

"No!" she emphatically replied. "I love him. Of course, I wouldn't do that!"

This was one of those moments where I could see my client's neurology changing as that shocked looked came over her face, and she realized what an unfounded fear she'd held on to.

Sylvia went home and began living a new story about her life based on living mindfully in the moment. Rather than letting old stories control her and hold her back, she gave them a new meaning and transformed them into sources of wisdom, resilience, and strength. She achieved her goal weight and stayed in contact for several years. She loved telling me about her slender and active life that she was living in her eighties.

How awesome is that?! For forty years, Sylvia had been holding on to excess weight to ensure that she'd remain faithful to the man she loved. Then she created a new story of faithfulness at a healthy weight.

You may be wondering how you will know that you are being your Best Self. Well, it's not a destination—it is a journey. There are moments when you are in the groove, and it just feels right being yourself. And there are other times when old thoughts, old emotions, and old patterns of behavior creep back in. Even in those moments when you are being the Greatest Expression of You, remember that you still have a pulse, and you still have more work to do.

When John was in his thirties, he came to me because his third marriage had just ended. John was depressed and angry. He wondered what was wrong with him that everyone he cared about left him.

As a small boy, he was close to his mom, and his parents had a loving, healthy marriage. Growing up, he became especially close to his dad. They hunted, fished, camped, and hiked all over the Cascades and Olympic Mountains. When John was thirteen, his father was killed in the Gulf War. Throughout junior high and high school, his mom suffered with depression and alcoholism. She was in and out of treatment centers and, at one point, was hospitalized in a psych ward. At the time I met John, he was still estranged from his mother.

For the first thirteen years of his life, he had a close-knit, loving family that was now suddenly torn apart. John spent much of his teen years living with an angry and abusive uncle. At thirteen, John's life of love, safety, and security became one of abandonment, grief, and mistrust.

As an adult, John and his wives had participated in many relationship counseling sessions. He learned that he didn't let people get close to him because he knew that if he did, they would abandon him. When someone said, "I love you," he didn't trust they'd stick around.

John and two of his friends had started a successful business, but he often fought with his partners and, at times, he sabotaged their efforts. John went so far as to say that if he messed up the relationship, then he would know that he had caused it to fall apart. Since he caused it, he didn't feel hurt and abandoned.

I introduced John to the concept of being the Greatest Expression of himself. I taught him self-hypnosis and other mindfulness-based tools so that he could fire and wire new neuropathways and live in the NOW rather than in his troubled past. That was more than ten years ago, and I still hear from John from time to time. He is happily married and has two young children. In our last chat, he told me about how he now starts each day by bundling the joys of his wedding day and births of each of his children into one big joy and memorizes that joy while meditating on being his **Best Self**.

Worldwide, neuroscientists have demonstrated that our brains are truly extraordinary; unlike computers, which are built to certain specifications and receive software updates periodically, your brain can receive hardware updates in addition to software updates. Your life experiences cause different pathways to form or to fall dormant; neuropathways are created and discarded, according to your experiences.

When you learn something new, you create new connections between your neurons. You rewire your brain to adapt to new circumstances. This happens daily, and get this: you can encourage and stimulate the changing of your neurology. That's what this book is all about: firing and wiring new neuropathways so that you can be **Your Best Self**.

By firing and wiring new neuropathways, not only can you change your mental and emotional relationship with yourself, but you can also change your relationship with the people you love: family, friends, colleagues. It can help you achieve your goals and improve your health. If you suffer with physical pain, just think how different life can be without the suffering!

You have a choice, so what will it be? Will you continue to think and feel the same old thoughts and emotions by telling yourself the old stories that you know and that are familiar to you? Or is it time to live joyfully in this moment and start writing a whole new story by thinking and feeling differently?

To give you something to look forward to, I've listed the eight steps of the Greatest Expression of You Daily Practice. As you continue reading, each of these steps will be described to you.

DAILY PRACTICE

1. **Begin each day by reading your** Greatest Expression of You. (You will have the opportunity to write your Greatest Expression of You in Chapter 4.)
2. **Remember Joy** and be joyful. (Chapter 5)
3. **Mentally rehearse** being joyful as you go about your day. Give thanks for being the Greatest Expression of You. (Chapter 6)
4. **Meditate** on joyfully being the Greatest Expression of You. (Chapter 7)
5. **Use self-hypnosis** throughout the day to remind yourself who it is you are becoming. (Chapter 8)
6. **Believe**: We only act on and out of what we personally believe to be true. (Chapter 9)
7. **Gratitude**: Give thanks for being the Greatest Expression of You and open yourself up to receiving. (Chapter 9)
8. **Inventory**: At the end of the day, take inventory of your day. Where did you do best at being the Greatest Expression of You? Where did you fall from grace? Mentally rehearse being and doing differently next time. (Chapter 10)

As you read on, I encourage you to use the daily practices and put your heart into the Greatest Expression of You. You will discover that you really can create your future to be greater than your past and that you can also use the Greatest Expression of You process to enhance activities in your daily life.

Chapter 2

Hardwired

"Every time you are tempted to react in the same old way, ask if you want to be a prisoner of the past or a pioneer of the future."
— Deepak Chopra

In Chapter 1, I introduced you to John. For the first thirteen years of his life, John had a happy and loving childhood. His dad's death shattered the idyllic childhood that he had known. The trauma of this great loss combined with a host of emotions (including grief, anger, hurt, fear, and sadness) fused with the belief that if he loved someone, they would abandon him. John's mom's struggle with depression and alcoholism proved that if he loved someone, he would be abandoned. For this young teen, this belief served as a demonstration of his resilience. With his limited life experience, this belief was what he could do to protect himself from the pain of hurt and abandonment.

John's reaction to love became hardwired. As lonely and as miserable as he was, this method of self-protection was what he knew. It was comfortable and had become hardwired—a habituated automatic response. In fact, when he did open his heart to let someone in, his body responded as if he was experiencing a chemical withdrawal. He felt fear and anxiety. That was the problem. The method he learned to protect himself as a young teen worked well then, but it does not work for him today.

How are you protecting yourself in ways that no longer serve you? What old emotional wounds are you still acting out that are hindering you from living a joyous life? What thoughts, emotions, and behaviors have you hardwired that no longer serve you? These habits literally shape your brain; how are they harming your life?

Neurons that Fire Together Wire Together

The human brain has more than one hundred billion nerve cells called neurons. These neurons are more powerful than the most powerful supercomputer in the world. When you have a thought, there is a spark between neurons. If you don't have the thought again, there is no connection of those neurons unless a powerful emotion is involved. If some form of trauma (real or imagined) is involved with the thought, the neurological connection becomes hardwired. The more you repeat the thought with a strong emotion, the more a connection is made—the neurons fire and wire together.

In other words, when we are thinking the same thoughts, experiencing the same emotions, and acting out the same behaviors, neurons in the body repeatedly fire and wire (connect) to each other, especially when emotion is involved. The more often you perform an action or behave a certain way, the more it gets physically wired into your brain. Your brain continuously adapts, grows, and rewires itself.

This remarkable adaptive quality of your brain can work both for and against you. The brain is like a muscle and, with practice and effort, you can strengthen the neural connections. And, like a muscle, if you don't use it, you lose it. A study of British civil servants showed that after retirement, short-term memory decreased by over 40 percent due to lack of mental stimulation.

The chemicals released as a response to thoughts and emotions are addictive. They become a habit, and they keep us stuck in the same patterns of behavior. Every time you act in the same way, a specific neuronal pattern is stimulated and reinforced.

Just like hiking a worn trail, your brain seeks efficiency, so it consistently takes the path of least resistance, creating a habit or an addiction. However, because of neuroplasticity, you can change the way your brain is wired by changing your thoughts, your emotions, and your habits with stimulation and challenge.

Making or breaking a habit involves neuroplastic change in your brain. Mental, emotional, and behavioral habits are developed in the cerebral cortex and, more specifically, the frontal lobe. It is the most recently evolved part of our brain and is often referred to as the "new brain." Once these habits are formed, they become embedded in the limbic system or "old" brain (aka lizard brain) which includes the amygdala, hippocampus, and hypothalamus that regulate our emotional responses. The old brain includes the brain stem that is responsible for our startle and fight-or-flight response. One problem is that the old brain cannot distinguish between threats that are real or imagined.

Neuroscience has proven that you can rewire or change your brain until the day you die. This ability to change your brain is called neuroplasticity. You can literally change your brain just by thinking differently.

Here is another way of understanding it: When you first learned to drive a car, you used your prefrontal cortex (your new brain) to turn the key and start the engine. Your prefrontal lobe is used for planning complex cognitive behavior, personality expression, decision-making, and moderating social behavior. You thought about each individual action: put the car in reverse, back up, step on the brake, shift into drive, drive to the corner, step on the brakes, put on the turn signal, turn the corner. All very frontal lobe, new brain conscious thoughts.

Today when you drive, the process has become automatic. You no longer consciously think about stepping on the brake; you just do it. Your old brain (the lizard brain) handles driving automatically. Your lizard brain is the basal ganglia that controls your innate and automatic self-preserving behavior patterns, ensuring your survival. You don't consciously think, "The pretty red lights of that car in front of me are illuminated, so I should step on the brake." You just do it. The action has become instinctual. Your body drives you; it's now the servant driving the master.

The same applies to personality traits like *Not Good Enough* or keeping people at a distance to avoid hurt and abandonment. Thoughts like these are not of the conscious mind. You don't wake up in the morning thinking that this is a great day to feel Not Good Enough; it's just your autopilot. Driving has become hardwired.

Being able to operate on autopilot can be great when it comes to riding a bike or driving your car. But does it serve you well in your relationships? Your career? Have you failed miserably at losing weight and keeping it off? What goals have you set for yourself and never achieved? Trying to change and yet keep the same old thoughts and emotions does not work.

Let's get back to John because there is something that I have yet to share about him. He had tried repeatedly through individual and relationship counseling to overcome his issues with abandonment and to allow people to love him. This resulted in him becoming physically ill from all the discomfort—physical, mental, and emotional—he experienced. When John tried not to fire those old neuropathways, he literally went into a chemical withdrawal.

These were the times when his drug and alcohol abuse was at its worst. His addiction to fear of abandonment was strong. He had not yet learned how to fire and wire new neuropathways that could allow him to have the loving relationships that he so desperately wanted.

As previously stated, your old brain does not know the difference between what it is thinking internally and what it is experiencing in its external environment.

In other words, if you are thinking that you are being chased by the saber-toothed tiger, your body cannot tell the difference between actually being chased or imagining being chased. If you imagine being chased by the tiger, your body produces the same chemicals as if you were literally being chased. If you worry about something awful happening, your body responds as if it is happening. The reality is that as much as 85 percent of what you worry about never happens.

Fortunately, the opposite is also true; if you imagine relaxing on a Maui beach with an equally intense level of emotion that you use to imagine fearful situations, your body produces the same brain-tranquilizing chemicals as if you were really relaxing on the beach.

When you memorize being the Greatest Expression of You—and that becomes your norm—you change your thoughts, your emotions, and as a result, your behavior. You create a new genetic expression that opens the path for health.

How You Use Your Mind Changes Your Brain

How you use your mind changes your brain for better or for worse. When you repeatedly think the same thoughts, the neurons become like a superhighway in your brain.

If you have been telling yourself the same self-defeating story over and over again, those thoughts have become hardwired. That story is now part of your personality; it is a part of your identity. You have those thoughts and live out the story of those thoughts automatically. Every time you think, feel, or do something, you strengthen a pathway. Habits are well-traveled pathways and your brain finds strengthening pathways easy to perform.

Now, knowing these hardwired thoughts become a part of your identity and personality, think for a moment about how you talk to yourself. Are you acknowledging yourself for all of your strengths and talents? Or are you, like most people, focused on your faults and fears?

When emotions embed experiences into long-term memory, problems arise. When you are faced with current obstacles in your life that require thinking and acting in new ways, and you use familiar feelings as a barometer for change, you will most certainly talk yourself out of your ideal. Your feelings reflect the past, but to change is to abandon past ways of thinking, acting, and feeling so that you can move into the future with a new outcome. To change is to think and act greater than how you feel. When emotions like anger, hurt, fear, and sadness are in your face, it can be really easy to fall back into the old ways of being because they are familiar and known from your past experience.

Simply put, when you are used to thinking and feeling a certain way, that way feels familiar, even if it also feels miserable. When you try to stop the misery, to be and do differently, your body goes into withdrawal, yearning for the familiar feeling of misery. This is where most people fail with change; they don't like how it feels to experience change. People may feel awkward, self-conscious, even anxious when experiencing something that is unfamiliar. Because change is uncomfortable, they remain addicted to the misery that they feel.

Rewiring Your Brain

Rewiring your brain is possible because of the neuroplastic nature of your brain. Your brain's innate capacity to grow new neurons and, more importantly, new connections among the neurons is lifelong. When you choose to rewire your brain's patterns, you are creating change by engaging in self-directed neuroplasticity.

Change isn't easy; when we want to commit to a goal, we start out with good intentions and ideas but, quite often, we return to unwanted habits. The concept of change requires that you do something differently within the same environment; you're not going to respond to your environment with your customary thoughts and reactions. That, however, is easier said than done. Many of us tend to think the same thoughts, have the same feelings, and follow the same routines throughout our life. The problem is that this causes you to keep using the same patterns and combinations of neural circuits in your brain, and they tend to become hardwired. This is how you create habits of thinking, feeling, and doing.

Hardwiring can be a good thing. Thanks to hardwiring, when you learn a new skill, such as driving a car, the more you practice, the more you hardwire what you learn into your brain's circuits. Eventually, you can operate a car automatically.

But if you want to change something in your life, you have to stop the brain from firing in the same old sequences and combinations. You need to create a new level of mind function by disconnecting the old neural circuits and rewiring your brain in new patterns of nerve cell connections. In other words, you must stop thinking and feeling the same old thoughts.

Building Neural Pathways

Studies at Yale show that your brain reflects what you think and feel, even if what you think and feel is not a true representation of what happened. Every minute of every day, your body is physically reacting and actually changing in response to the thoughts that run through your mind. You are building neural pathways with every thought and every feeling.

In 1972, Canadian researcher Hans Selye proved that stress affects the weakest link of the body first. We can't say that stress causes a disease such as cancer, but stress is like a watering can and fertilizer in one that augments the environment in which a disease can grow.

If fear and negativity are what you are thinking and feeling, then you are building a neural network of *dis*-ease. You are literally rewriting the expression of your genes every second with your thoughts, emotions, and actions. When you fire and wire the same thoughts and emotions, you are building the corresponding neuropathways. When you stop firing those same neuropathways, they will stop firing and "un-wire." How exciting is that?! You do not have to live the rest of your life with the same old thoughts, emotions, and behaviors.

You Can Change

When we met in 2009, Marcia had irritable bowel syndrome, high blood pressure, type II diabetes, and was ninety pounds overweight. She was depressed, stressed, anxious, and frequently experienced panic attacks. Marcia's primary goal was to lose weight, but she knew that she had to gain control over the depression, stress, and anxiety. Marcia had dieted many times to lose weight and had, according to her, "failed miserably." Weight loss seemed hopeless but, as a last resort, she was willing to give hypnosis a half-hearted try.

Marcia said that she had a good childhood but that demonstrations of love, affection, and approval were few and far between. As a young girl, Marcia loved baking frosted sugar cookies with her aunt, who was always accepting, kind, and loving. Fat, salt, and sugar became entwined with love and acceptance, which would haunt her later in life.

Her dad worked hard and mostly ignored her. Marcia's mom was always pushing her to do better. Marcia knew that her mom's heart was in the right place, but she was highly critical and demanded perfection. Achieving an A- was not acceptable, and she expected Marcia to make first chair violin in the school orchestra, class president, and head cheerleader. Marcia's mom put her on her first diet when she was in grade school and constantly commented on Marcia's weight into adulthood.

Marcia internalized her mom's criticisms: "What's the matter with you? You can do better than that. You have to work harder." And even though Marcia became head cheerleader as a senior in high school, her mom told her that she was too fat to dress in short skirts and cheer in front of her classmates. In college, Marcia became anxious and experienced her first panic attack.

Today, when Marcia looks at those cheerleading photos, she realizes that she was at a perfectly healthy weight.

Marcia had hardwired food with love and acceptance. She had hardwired the belief that she had to be perfect with depression, stress, and anxiety. Before I ever had a chance to talk with her about it, she told me that any time she tried to relax, she felt uneasy and jittery. She said that dieting made her more anxious and depressed. Her body was addicted to the adrenalin and cortisol caused by stress, and it was addicted to food as love. Marcia went into withdrawal when she tried to relax and when she tried to eat healthy.

Over the next year, as Marcia started thinking and feeling differently, she released the ninety pounds. I taught her the tools she needed to navigate her way through the withdrawal by replacing the adrenalin and cortisol with endorphins, serotonin, dopamine, and norepinephrine. In other words, she replaced depression and anxiety with feeling calm and happy. She fired and wired new thoughts and emotions and changed her behavior. The irritable bowel syndrome was no longer present, the diabetes subsided, and her blood pressure reached a healthy level. Marcia was calm, relaxed, and hadn't felt anxious or had a panic attack in months.

I last heard from Marcia in 2019. She now personifies her Greatest Expression and lives a happy, productive life filled with love and joy. What a transformation!

Marcia is one example of many people who have changed their life by incorporating the Greatest Expression of You process into their life.

What about you; do you want to change? If you are ready and willing, you too can become your best self.

Chapter 3

You Can Fire and Wire New Neuropathways

"There are far better things ahead than any we leave behind."
— C.S. Lewis

Life's a Play

In *As You Like It,* Shakespeare's monologue compares life to a play. Let's pretend that there in your personal life theatre are all the various parts of you: the newborn, the five-year-old, the eighteen-year-old, the thirty, the fifty, the sixty-year-old and so on.

You also notice that there on your theatre stage is the son or daughter version of you, the sibling, the student, the spouse, the parent. The worker is there, as are the professional, the friend, the gardener, the knitter, the overeater, the cyclist, and more. All of the various aspects of yourself are there in your theater.

Amongst these characters of your life's story exist parts of yourself that you may not like so much as well as your beloved unique qualities. All together, they make up who you are today. If you were to eliminate any one of these characters, your life story would no longer make sense. It would be like in the movie, *It's a Wonderful Life*. When George Bailey no longer existed, life in Bedford Falls no longer made sense.

It's important not to try to remove any one of these characters from your life. No matter how much misery the twenty-year-old you may have caused, they helped shape who you are today, and they are an important influence on who you are becoming.

Each of the past parts of you, even the ones you don't like or aren't proud of, is a significant part of your life story. They have become hardwired neuropathways. Sometimes these parts serve as demonstrations of notable qualities such as strength or resilience. A past part may have helped you at some point in life to survive, even though today that same part may be holding you back or even killing you.

My hope is that by the time you finish reading this book, you will know how you can write a new script—a new story that serves you better—for each of these characters that make up who you are today.

You Have a Plastic Brain

When I talk with clients about the plastic brain, I'm usually met with a curious look and a raised eyebrow. The concept of a plastic brain is relatively new, and many people have never heard of neuroplasticity.

Your brain is a living organ that can change and can be rewired through thoughts, emotions, and behavior. Throughout your life, your brain can form new neural connections.

In 1890, American psychologist William James first wrote about the theory of neuroplasticity in his book *The Principles of*

Psychology. The term neuroplasticity was first used in 1948 by the Polish Neuroscientist Jerzy Konorski.

In recent years, advancements in modern technology have enabled researchers to document how your brain can change. Neuroplasticity is responsible for all permanent learning that takes place in your brain. It is the process by which you learn a new language or to play a musical instrument, recover from an injury, overcome depression and addiction, overcome birth abnormalities, or recover from a stroke. Additionally, neuroplasticity makes your brain more resilient.

Create Your Future to Be Greater than Your Past

Your brain contains about eighty-six billion neurons that can fire and wire in trillions of combinations. These neurons change in response to thoughts, emotions, environmental stimuli, illness, and injury. By manipulating these neurons, you can rewire your brain to overcome severe physical, mental, and emotional challenges.

Neuroscience has shown that thinking activates genes that prompt neurons to form new connections. We know that imagination itself can produce brain changes; the mere act of thinking about an action produces the same brain changes as actually performing the action.

New thoughts and skills carve out new pathways. Repetition and practice strengthen these pathways, forming new habits, while pathways that get used less weaken. Rewiring your brain is possible with repeated and direct attention towards a desired change.

You can create changes in your brain rather quickly; studies have shown that habits can be formed in as little as seven days of repeated activity. However, these studies show that changes can dissipate just as easily. In other words, if you don't use it, you lose it.

Rewire Your Neurology

We all know that doing the same old thing over and over again and expecting different results is insanity. We also know that when nothing changes, *nothing changes.*

Neuroscience teaches us that we can rewire our neurology; we can produce change at any age just by thinking differently.

Neuroscientist Alvaro Pascual-Leone conducted a study at Harvard Medical School in 2003[1] where they divided people that had never played the piano into two groups. One half of the group physically played one-handed finger exercises for two hours a day for five days. The second half of the group mentally rehearsed the same finger exercises in their mind for the same amount of time. This second group did not actually play the exercises on the keyboard.

The group that mentally rehearsed grew the same amount of brain connections as the group that physically played the finger exercises on the piano. The before and after functional brain scans showed new areas of the same region of the brain had expanded in both groups. Both groups created new brain circuits.

This Harvard study, along with other research, shows that your brain does not know the difference between what is happening in your imagination and what is happening in the external world.

---

[1] Bangert, Marc and Altenmüller, Eckart O. 2003 "Mapping Perception to Action in Piano Practice: A Longitudinal DC-EEG Study" https://dash.harvard.edu/bitstream/handle/1/4734539/270043.pdf?sequence=1

Not only can mental training change the physical structure of your brain, but your brain does also not differentiate between real or imagined events.

Your Mind Can Change Your Body

Research has shown that when you change your mind, you also create change in your body. These studies have shown that there is an actual mind-body connection and that the mind changes the body. This is known as *bioplasticity*.

"Bioplasticity is consciousness or the mind's ability to alter or heal the body, including the brain."[2] Your body has the ability to adapt and change as it responds to your thoughts, your emotions, and your behaviors.

For example, subjects in one study were asked to do a finger exercise against the resistance of a spring over the course of four weeks for an hour a day. They showed a 30 percent increase in muscle strength.

A second group of subjects never actually did the finger exercise. They mentally practiced the same activity for the same length of time, and this group had a 22 percent increase in muscle strength without any physical activity. The body became stronger from mental rehearsal.

Both the piano study and the resistance spring study show that your thoughts can create physical changes in your body.

Play With Me

Imagine or pretend being in your kitchen for a moment. On the counter is a basket of lemons. You gently squeeze the lemons

---

[2] Joseph Sansone, *Bioplasticity:* Hypnosis Mind Body Healing, p.159, High Energy Publishing LLC, Kindle Edition 2014

and select the one that has a good feel and place it on your cutting board. You take out your favorite knife and slice this juicy lemon in half.

You begin cutting through one of the halves, and you feel the spray of the lemon juice across the back of your hands. The tart fragrance of lemon wafts upward, and you smell it.

As you slice through one of the quarters of lemon, you notice the sun glistening off the lemon juice that is running off the cutting board onto the counter.

With two fingers, you raise one of the wedges to your mouth and bite it away from the peel. Feel the spray of the lemon juice in your mouth.

Now notice, do you have more or less saliva in your mouth? Did your jaws tighten? Do you smell lemon? What else did you notice from imagining biting into the lemon?

Wait a minute. There is no lemon, just you reading about a lemon. But as you imagined biting into the lemon, your body started producing the same response as if it were real!

Imagined Stress and Your Health

As with the lemon experience, your body cannot tell the difference between you imagining a stressful event or actually experiencing a stressful event. You can worry and fret all night about all that *might* happen only to find that nothing you worried about ever came to be. All that needless stress creates toxins in your body that build up over time.

This ongoing perceived stress can cause a host of problems for your body:

- Impair cognitive performance
- Suppress thyroid function
- Cause blood sugar imbalance
- Decrease bone density
- Raise blood pressure
- Lower immunity
- Increase abdominal fat
- And numerous other health challenges

All of these impair your health. If your body doesn't know the difference between whether you actually eat a lemon or only imagine it and if your body doesn't know that what you are worrying about isn't going to happen but produces cortisol in response as if it is happening, you are thinking yourself sick.

Change Your Physiology

While this book is about how you can change your thoughts and emotions to create a future that is greater than your past, I'd be remiss if I didn't mention the influences that your body has on your thoughts and emotions. Just as you imagine biting into a lemon creates physical responses in your body, when you change your physiology, you change how you think and feel.

Perhaps you have noticed that injury, chronic pain, disease, and lack of sleep can cause depression, lethargy, and hopelessness. Are you aware of how much of what you eat and drink affects your thoughts and emotions?

For instance, medical researchers have shown that chocolate is like a whole drugstore of mild opiates, caffeine, amphetamine-like components all mixed with a whiff of marijuana. Chocolate and other foods containing fat and sugar hit the exact same opiate receptors as heroin and cause a habituation that is as real as addiction to narcotics. The Standard American Diet (SAD) is loaded with processed foods containing fat, salt, and sugar that can lead to depression and dull your mind.

Drinking water, eating whole grains, vegetables, and fruit can sharpen your thinking and elevate your mood. Any cardio activity is the most effective anti-anxiety agent and anti-depressant available to us today.

Eating whole plant-based food, drinking plenty of water, and getting up and moving your body can go a long way toward helping you to become the **Greatest Expression of You**.

Another excellent way to change your physiology is by stimulating your vagus nerve. The vagus nerve is a squiggly, shaggy, branching nerve connecting most of the major organs between the brain and colon, and it is the longest nerve in the body. It gets its name from "vagabond" because it wanders through your body like a system of roots or phone lines. The vagus nerve is the mind-body connection and has the responsibility of mediator between thinking and feeling. The vagus nerve has been described as the queen of the parasympathetic nervous system.

When you properly activate your vagus nerve, you can reduce or even stop the effects of the sympathetic nervous system, which is the "fight-or-flight" stress-releasing adrenaline/ cortisol survival mode. When you stimulate your vagus nerve with deep breathing, you relax and enter the "rest and digest" state, which has the benefits of boosting your immune response, calming your mind, and promotes emotional equanimity.

A quick Google search of the vagus nerve will show you a multitude of ways that you can activate your vagus nerve. Here are two of my favorite ways to stimulate the vagus nerve:

1. There is a part of the vagus nerve at the roof of the mouth behind your front teeth. When we put our tongue there, usually by instinct, it stimulates your vagus nerve and calms tension.

2. I like this breathing exercise as it's quick, easy, and powerfully effective:

a. Slowly breathe in through your nose to a count of three, bringing your breath deep into your body, about three fingers below your navel, midway between your front and your back.

b. Hold your breath to a count of three.

c. Slowly exhale to a count of five.

d. Repeat this cycle three to five times.

I invite you make a habit of activating your vagus nerve several times every day. It's a great way to feel better, think better, and find more joy in your life.

Think Yourself Well

If you can think yourself sick, can you create change in your health by thinking differently? Imagine what might be possible.

Neuroscientists tell us that you can. Just as you can increase muscle strength, activate stress hormones, and even taste and smell a lemon using the power of your mind, think about what may be possible when you use bioplasticity to heal from cancer, autoimmune disease, or chronic pain.

When I first heard from Frank, he was desperate. He needed a medical procedure performed on his heart, but he had white coat syndrome. Any time a medical professional took his blood pressure, his numbers went off the charts. However, when he checked at home, his blood pressure was at a healthy level.

In our first session, Frank spoke about the major stressors in his life: his business and a son who was in and out of rehab for drug addiction. He was not sleeping and was suffering with self-doubt, fear, anxiety, and depression. He revealed that as a young boy, he desperately tried to intercede in the fights between his father and alcoholic mother. Frank had been living his life in desperation.

In our sessions, Frank learned stress reduction techniques and self-hypnosis. I also taught him how to stimulate his vagus nerve using breathing techniques. He emailed his Greatest Expression to me:

"I am a child of God held safely and securely in his arms of love."

Within a few weeks, Frank called me as he was driving home from a medical appointment. A few minutes after having his blood pressure checked, his physician commented on how good it was to see his blood pressure was normal. At that moment, Frank realized that he had forgotten his old habit of white coat syndrome. Soon, Frank was sleeping again. He was experiencing joy in his life. His relationship with his son improved, and his wife was thrilled to have the man she fell in love with back in her life.

Two months after our first session, the doctor told Frank they should hold off for a while on the heart procedure. Frank didn't fully understand why until about four months later when his doctor told him the procedure was no longer needed. Frank had changed his thoughts, emotions, and behaviors; his body changed accordingly. With tears in his eyes, he shared with me that he finally understood Proverbs 23:7 "For as a person thinketh in their heart, so is he or she."

Are You Reading from the Same Old Script?

Are you reading from the same old script? Here is what I mean: A four-year-old is feeling sad, ignored, and lonely. They are looking for love. Grandma gives them a hug and one of her homemade chocolate chip cookies. Unconditional love and acceptance anchor with touch as well as with the fat, salt, and sugar. These hit the child's opiate receptors like heroin.

At age four, the unconscious mind learned that food like chocolate chip cookies equates with love and comfort. Comfort food becomes the go-to for making it through life.

Years later, that grown child may find themself feeling sad, ignored, and lonely, but Grandma isn't there anymore to give the hug. Turning to food, the grown child quickly devours cookies and other comfort foods, resulting in obesity, diabetes, high blood pressure, cancer, autoimmune diseases, and other illnesses.

That four-year-old is an important part of this person's life, but where they run into trouble is when that four-year-old reads from the same old script and directs the same old scene over and over again.

A woman from Montreal named Sheila contacted me for hypnosis for stress, anxiety, depression, and alcohol abuse. She is a single mom in a highly-paid and demanding leadership role at a tech company. When she first contacted me, her anxiety had progressed to panic attacks and sleepless nights. She had become rageful with her children and with a few of her colleagues.

In our sessions, Sheila revealed that she was the youngest of five children and that as a young girl, there were always crises and tense times in her family. If she was "too happy," she was ridiculed and then ignored. Her mom was often depressed and spent a great deal of time in bed. At about age three or four, Sheila learned that to get any attention, she had to throw a temper tantrum. In junior high, she started faking test anxiety so that her mom would dote on her and give her special attention. In these moments of her mom comforting her, Shelia felt loved and cared for, whereas if she was calm and happy, she was ignored.

What started out as a survival technique and demonstration of her resilience became hardwired in Sheila's neurology. As an adult, she did not wake up each morning and make the decision that it was a great day to be anxious, have panic attacks, and be angry. These traits had become automatic. They were familiar and even comfortable. When she tried to relax and be happy, she felt uneasy and became anxious. She had become addicted to anger and anxiety, which was being compounded by depression and alcohol abuse.

Sheila was excited to learn about hypnosis and neuroplasticity, and she eagerly took to the Greatest Expression of You process. Within the first month, she reported significant improvement. At three months, she was happy, laughing, and couldn't remember the last time she was rageful with her kids or colleagues. Sheila also reported that she was now spending more quality time with her family and that she was more productive at both home and work. We never really addressed the alcohol abuse; she chose to quit drinking altogether. Sheila has lost twenty pounds and is back at her healthy ideal weight. Being her best self, she now strives to live a new script: a new story based on each moment.

Just like Sheila, there have been times in your life when a significant event occurred, and you made up a story to explain or understand why it happened. Being human, you began to live your life as if your story were true, and that story became part of your identity. You used that story as a survival technique and believed it was keeping you safe. The truth is these stories stopped you from getting the results you have wanted for your life. In reality, they're just stories you made up by attaching made-up meanings to events.

Where in your life have you been living the same old scripts that no longer serve you? When do you become defensive or angry for no real reason? Do you feel hurt or sad when others do not meet your expectations? What do you avoid or not do in your life because you have the belief that you are Not Good Enough? What decisions did you make as a young child that still run your life today? Did it ever occur to you not to believe everything that you think? Your thoughts are not truth.

Remembered Wellness

Harvard Medical School Professor Dr. Herbert Benson coined the term "Remembered wellness," which emphasizes the fact that being well is your natural state. Your body and mind seek wellness and equilibrium. Believe it or not, wellness is your natural state. Dis-ease, depression, and anxiety are physical, mental, and emotional incarnations of disruption of this natural state. My friend and colleague Michael Ellner taught me that the body was created to be healthy, and it was created to heal.

Consider this: You are an amazingly successful product of nature. Your very existence is an unbroken genetic chain between you and the beginning of life. The survival and thriving successes of all your ancestors who survived saber-toothed tigers, ice ages, diseases, famines, and millennia of wars are embedded in your genetic code. When you are being your Best Self, you are activating your natural propensity for wellness.

When you are thinking and feeling the old thoughts and emotions that no longer serve you, you are remembering the unnatural state of illness. When you fire and wire new neuropathways by being the Greatest Expression of You, you activate your body's natural abilities to heal.

Write a New Script

Today, like Sheila, you are able to write a whole new script based upon this moment. You truly can create your future to be greater than your past.

Now, wiggle your toes, wiggle your butt; take a deep breath in through your nose and let it out through your mouth. Thank all the various parts of you for getting you to this point in your life. Remember that the events of the past are not happening in this moment now.

Let the young child part of you know that today you will give yourself time to play with the puppy, with the grandchildren. Or perhaps you will take time to watch a favorite movie on Netflix.

I encourage you now to pick one thing in your life that you want to change. As an example, maybe you don't make your needs and wishes known because you avoid conflict. Maybe you want to lose weight but, because of past failures, you think that you can never be successful. Or maybe you are thinking, "I don't deserve to have a loving relationship, to get good grades, to have money, or ..."

Write down your thoughts, your limiting beliefs, and emotions about what you want to change. As you do this, identify the stories or lies you are telling yourself. Understand that you created these lies by giving meanings to events but that they are not the truth about you. Again, just because you think it does not make it true.

If you are ready to think, feel, and do differently, read on.

Chapter 4

What is the Greatest Expression of You?

"It all begins with how you choose to think. When you change the way you look at things, the things you look at change."
—Dr. Wayne Dyer

In the previous chapters, I have talked about the Daily Practice for being the Greatest Expression of You, but first, you really do need to know just what that is.

What is the Greatest Expression of You? If you are like most people to whom I ask this question, you may be struggling for an answer. In Chapter 1, I described the Greatest Expression as being **Your Best Self**. I also shared my use of the phrase "God, let me be as good as Luna thinks that I am" as part of my daily morning prayer and meditation and to help create mental and emotional space. If I can be as good as she thinks I am, I'm having a great day!

Another way of thinking about this is to reflect on how children in your life (your children or grandchildren, nieces, or nephews) thought of you when they were around three or four years old.

During that age of innocence, they looked to you for love and protection, and they loved you unconditionally. Remember how, when you walked through the doorway, they would come running with their arms up, excited to see you? The look in their eyes was of unconditional love, adoration, excitement, and joy.

Our children and pets are not interested in what we do—it's who we are being that matters. Doing is what you do. Doing is feeding your dog, holding your child, worrying when your teen is out too late.

Doing is also that mindset that I referred to as salvation by good works. This is frequently goal-oriented and driven by the desire to diminish the perceived gap between how things are and how we think we need them to be. Often, when you are in the doing mode, you have a sense of "have to," "must," "should," "ought," or "need to." I don't know about you, but when I am wrapped up in the *doing,* I'm probably *being* Not Enough. That's when I am thinking that if I only worked harder or did more or if I'd just done this differently or better or tried harder, I would be enough.

Mary had a common response when I asked her about her best self. She started listing off things that she does: spend time with her kids, pay attention to her husband, prepare healthy and interesting meals for her family, volunteer at her church's food bank, drive her elderly neighbor to the doctor. I cut her off at that point as it was clear the list of her doing was going to be long. As we talked, it became clear that her identity was wrapped up in what she did and not in who she is.

I could tell that she was struggling with her self-identity and the realization that she had tied it to what she did. I asked her to share with me her two favorite things from her list.

Mary shared that she most enjoyed spending time with the kids and handing out food at the food bank. Sometimes she took her kids to the food bank, and they would help her by collecting canned food and boxes of cereal and filling grocery bags. As she spoke, her face lit up, and her eyes sparkled; her cheeks became rosier, and her smile grew from ear to ear.

"What are you feeling right now?" I asked.

"Love, joy, caring, and grateful," she responded.

I then asked if these words described her beingness.

Without hesitation, she said, "Oh yes!"

"So, what is your greatest expression?" I asked.

Her response was, "I am a loving, joyful, caring, and grateful mom."

I told her that this was an awesome start. I assigned her homework: give this some thought over the next few days and write one to three sentences that describe her best self. I also suggested that she consider leaving the word *mom* out of it.

Two days later, I received a text with a photo of a sticky note on her bathroom mirror that read, "I am filled with love and overflowing with joy and gratitude. I am happiest when I share these blessings."

I texted back, "WOW!! Now own that!"

Another time, my eyes filled with tears of joy when a man who had been previously wrapped up in self-doubt and self-loathing came into my office and read his Greatest Expression to me:

"I am a spark of God. Limitless joy, love, and success flow through me."

What an amazing way to start your day: by reminding yourself that you are a *spark of God!* How awesome is that?!

Being is who you are at your core and in your heart. It's what's underneath all of the doing. It's characterized by your personal qualities and the direct, immediate, intimate experience of the present. *Doing* is more future-oriented, and *being* is more in the moment. *Being* is the place from which you do your *doing*.

If you were being the person that your dog or the young child in your life thinks you are, who would you be? How would you love? How would you feel? How would you think? How would you live?

How are you *being* in this world? What would you do differently than you do now? Being this person, how would you feel about yourself? How would your relationships with others be different? Would you be loving, kind, joyful, passionate, or radiant?

When I first sent people home to contemplate and to write their Greatest Expression, I began receiving two and three-page documents. These epistles were heartening to read, but I realized they weren't functional. I had first come to this realization when I found a six-page mission statement that I wrote for myself in the late 1990s. The statement had been lost in a file drawer, and I hadn't looked at it in years. Glancing with fresh eyes, it was clear to me that the lengthy document was too cumbersome to be a practical guide for my life. To be functional, a mission statement or the Greatest Expression of You should be no more than three sentences in length.

The Path

In her book, *The Path,* Laurie Beth Jones teaches us that a mission statement should be no more than two or three sentences in length, understandable to a seven-year-old, and you should be able to recite it when you are under pressure. Now, that is useful.

When I ask clients to write their Greatest Expression, I now specifically ask for two or three sentences. When their Greatest Expression is short and to the point, it becomes more useful as well as more meaningful to you. You can easily read something that is two or three sentences every morning as you brush your teeth, whereas most of us are not going to read several pages.

Examples of the Greatest Expression of You

Below are actual examples of Greatest Expression statements that people have given me permission to share. Use these to stimulate your own thoughts, and I encourage you to not use them word for word. Be your own Greatest Expression—not someone else's.

- I am a compassionate and passionate soul who is strong in the storm and who embraces challenges with tenacity and poise every day. I listen with my heart and practice skills that allow me to walk through life with self-confidence. God has created me in His image.
- I take on what the world offers me with good humor, compassion, and agency.
- I am a free-spirited, confident, and caring individual not bound by what others think. I feel no need to be defined by others or to be held to others' expectations of me, and I encourage others to do the same. My heart is at the forefront of my relationships, and I'm a loving and caring person regardless of what I or anyone else may think.
- I am spunky! I am respected! I am strong! I am energetic! ☺

- I am a happy guy who's active, appealing, energetic, and lives to expose my energy. I love my husband, dogs, and those that are truly valuable. I am giving in many ways.
- I am a loving and joyful Baba.
- I am pure positive energy, and I am one with my source.
- Through the eyes of my inner being, I bask in the perfection of me.
- I am filled with love and overflowing with joy, gratitude. I am happiest when I share these blessings.
- Loving me fully and believing in my unique humanity—with confidence, courage, self-respect, and honor—is the pathway to loving others, true strength, being happy, and having an extraordinary life. I am curious, fun-loving, adventurous, creative, honest, and generous.
- I radiate light and love and know the radiance of others. I fly because I am grounded. I see because I am. I exercise my body and being, and thus I am profoundly alive.
- I am fearless, loving, and full of energy. I'm positive, centered, and generous with others and with myself.
- I radiate warmth and compassion for all beings. I am responsible, loyal, and hardworking.
- I am blessed in this life. Today as I continue to help others, I also remember to help myself.
- I am a leader who is loving and compassionate.
- I am beautiful, sexy, and fun. I am elegant and graceful. I am intelligent and influential.
- I am a fun and loving person. I am faithful, honest, and dependable. I have a God-given happy spirit that brings others joy and comfort.

- My best self is LOVE. When I feel Loved by God, I radiate LOVE to everyone I encounter. My best self is peaceful, generous, and not wanting anything but to live another day to LOVE.
- I am my best when I believe in myself, in the goodness inherent in me.
- I am peaceful, filling people's hearts with content and happiness everywhere I go. I am excited for my future; I am successful and outgoing. I am true at heart; people look to me for confidence and love.
- Daily, I live my life filled with love, empathy, and passion for others and myself. I seek out opportunities to utilize my creative side and thrive in their successful completion. My compassion for animals has filled my heart and soul with love.
- I am a selfless man who loves, protects, and cares for his family first. I act with integrity in all my relationships. I am a good person.
- I am a child of Grace. I have a loving Jesus that loves me fully so that, in turn, I can love myself and others.
- I am a high-spirited adventurer who is confident, hardworking, and excited for the future. I'm a pretty cool dude.
- I am creating a life of unconditional love and compassion, exuberant joy, and infinite creativity. I allow myself to live fully right here, right now, in acceptance and surrender and peace. I live in gratitude, faith, integrity, and beauty.
- I am wildly creative and peaceful. I am caring, sensitive, playful, and funny.

- Success flows easily and abundantly to me in all forms. I am worthy of it, and I am gratefully and thankfully accepting it.
- I am gracefully evolving emotionally and spiritually into my best health toward meaningful contribution and fulfillment.
- I sing through today with *JOY* in my heart!
- I live in gratitude for the love and abundance in my life. I express this love daily to others in what I say and what I do. In this expression of love, my joy is amplified boundlessly.
- I am loved and loving. I radiate with warmth and confidence. I am glowing with a positive energy that spreads to the world around me. I am grateful and humbled by the abundance in my life.
- I am a spark of God. Limitless joy, love, and success flow through me.
- I am energetic, I am happy, and I am social.
- I see/feel the Magnificent Amy as—I feel light, I AM light—internally, externally, physically, and psychologically. I can FEEL the connection to all that is around me. I am bouncing slightly on the balls of my feet. I have released all of my excess weight and now move easily and gracefully. I am smiling broadly inside and quietly outside. I am happy. I feel both content and very alive. I have just finished the ride of a lifetime and am so ready for the next one that is in front of me.
- I thrive in love, abundance, and creativity.
- I feel love. Each day feels like a gift to me, and I remember that each day when I arise.
- I have joy, joy, joy down in my heart!

- I am a fun-loving, outgoing, witty, and adventurous person. I build connections in life with people that make me a better person. I live to be outdoors and breathe in the natural world around me. My family and my friends are at the heart of all I do.
- When I talk to someone, I listen, understand. I check with others for clarity as I am aware the misunderstandings are normal. I enjoy interesting dialogues with others. And I really love to connect with other people. Relationships are important to me. I do what I say I will do, keeping my word. My communication with all people stems from love and care about people. When I talk to others, I speak from my heart—honestly and caringly. I practice the use of words that allow others to have their own voice and opinions, allowing them to open up.
- I am a healthy balance of joyful giving, honest listening, and wild, genuine collaboration.
- I look forward to amazing adventures. I forgive the past and look forward to what life has to offer. I give care to myself, inside and out.
- I am strong and flexible. I am full of energy.
- I am at the helm, feeling completely confident and at ease. It is natural for me to give and receive love unconditionally. I am smiling. I am free. I am alive.
- I thrive on my inner joy, and I share it with all that I come in contact with. The energy of my joy is soft and comfortable, and effortless. My joy fills me with the confidence that I have all the wisdom, experience, and knowledge, but not necessarily the answers, to help myself or others in every part of my life.

- I am at ease and confident, attentive to all that surrounds me, loving, deep and quiet, love my body and what it can do, loyal friend/partner/mother, awesome problem solver, vivacious, sexy, intuitive, full of joy, tenacious, a frightening she-bear when those I love are in peril, trustworthy, childlike insatiable curiosity! I dig this woman.
- I expand in abundance, success, and love every day as I inspire those around me to do the same.
- I show up and be my best. I live in integrity with love, compassion, and joy.
- I am a happy, healthy, confident person with a zest for life and a deep faith and trust in God.
- Success flows easily and abundantly to me in all forms. I am worthy of it, and I am gratefully and thankfully accepting it.

Your Turn

Hopefully, you've been thinking about your own Greatest Expression. I now invite you to write down your response to these questions:

- What is the Greatest Expression of You?
- If you were being the person that your dog or the young child in your life thinks you are, who would you be?
- If you were to be your best self, who are you?
- How would you love?
- How would you feel? How would you think?
- How would you live?
- How are you being in this world?
- As your best self, what would you be doing differently than you are now?

- Being this person, how do you feel about yourself?
- How would your relationships with others be different? Are you loving, kind, joyful, passionate, or radiant?

After answering these questions, I encourage you to write out two or three sentences that describe your best self. Do not worry about getting it perfect.

What did you write? I really would love to know, so please email your Greatest Expression to me at: Roger@HypnosisHealthInfo.com.

If you decide in a day or two that you don't like a word or phrase, cross it out and change it. This is not the Ten Commandments written in stone. This will evolve just as you will evolve. What's important is that you start now.

I encourage you to write your Greatest Expression on a sticky note and post it on your bathroom mirror. Read it every morning as you brush your teeth and meditate on it as you wash your face, brush your hair, and prepare for your adventures of the day.

Why Am I Doing This?

You may be wondering why you are doing this. The Greatest Expression of You is all about creating your future to be greater than your past by repeatedly firing and wiring new neurons together with enough emotion so that they hardwire.

My experience is that most of us go through life thinking, feeling, and behaving as we always have because it's what we know, it's familiar, and it's comfortable. This is called *Neurorigidity*. It's like running on autopilot. Neurorigidity is that definition of insanity: thinking, feeling, and doing the same old things and expecting different results. I think that most people routinely think the same thoughts and perform the same actions while secretly expecting something different to show up in their lives. The good news is that functional imagery has shown that you can change your brain by thinking differently.

Your brain only knows what you tell it—so tell it a good story about your Best Self. By thinking differently, you cause your brain to fire in new sequences, patterns, and combinations. By making your brain work differently, you are literally changing your mind.

But let's step back for a moment. The Greatest Expression of You is far more than just thinking positively or half-heartedly repeating affirmations. For lasting change, it's not enough just to think differently—to just have "happy thoughts." Many people have confused positive thinking with magical and wishful thinking. Wishful thinking can be self-destructive when people establish unrealistic expectations. Thinking good thoughts is not going to give you the winning mega lottery number, especially if you don't buy a ticket. It's not enough to ace an exam—you have to attend class and study the material. Achieving positive results requires both optimism and positive action. It's not enough to only think positively about building strong muscles. In addition to purchasing a gym membership you do have to show up and press the iron.

Positive magical thinking can be a tyranny that leads to heartache and distress. You are overvaluing the power of your thoughts with the message that your thoughts are responsible for creating your health, well-being, and reality. Sadly, this can leave you feeling to blame when something bad happens to you. I know people who have died from AIDS, cancer, and other diseases who suffered from devastating guilt because they felt that they didn't think positive enough.

Positive thinking or even being the Greatest Expression of You does not mean that you have a guarantee that things will always go well. Nor does it mean that you will never experience anger, hurt, fear, sadness, and pain. Your resilience comes from experiencing these emotions, and they delineate your values. You don't feel anger, hurt, fear, or sadness about things you don't care about. People who try to bury these emotions under happy thoughts are denied the opportunity to learn about who they are and miss opportunities for personal growth. Physical, mental, emotional, and spiritual pain can open your heart to be compassionate and understanding.

Dark thoughts like "Not good enough" and painful emotions can be channeled to be your best teachers and illuminate what you value most, helping you to guide you in your journey to become your Best Self.

The Greatest Expression of You is not at all about being happy instead of sad or about experiencing joy instead of sorrow. I refer to it as "both and." You can be joyous *and* experience loss, sorrow, grief, or heartache. Being the Greatest Expression of You, you can walk with painful emotions *and* have joy.

Think of it this way: the greatest habit you will ever break is the habit of being yourself. With my Greatest Expression of You process: you can create the habit of being your best self. You have the ability to remodel your brain, but it takes repetition coupled with powerful emotion.

This experience is about creating a new reality which is why it is so important that you do it every day. For me, the process involved stepping out of the old myth of "I'm Not Good Enough" and into a new reality of being the loving guy Luna thinks I am.

What if you started each day with, "I have joy, joy, joy down in my heart!?" Just imagine how splendid that would be!

Congratulations! Hopefully, you now have your Greatest Expression of You. Read on and find out how you can use it to rewire your brain.

Chapter 5

Joyfully Be

"Make a joyful noise unto the Lord."
—Psalms 100

If you are one of my clients, you know I frequently talk about joy. Why joy? Think for a moment about a stressful or upsetting event in your life. Notice your thoughts and emotions. Do a quick body scan and notice the physical sensations in your body. Notice where you feel those sensations.

While you reflect on that upsetting event, say the word, *Joy*. Do you notice that you have a hard time staying with the upset feeling? Take it a bit further now and recall a joyful time or event in your life. Notice your thoughts, your emotions, and the physical sensations of joy in your body, becoming aware of the changes within your body, your thoughts, and your emotions.

Reflect on this for a moment. Do you and the people in your life talk more about your joys and the abundance in your life, or do you talk more about what's wrong in your life and in this world? Robert T. Sears, S.J., Ph.D., wrote, "Joy is a great risk. It requires us to let go of complaining, putting ourselves down, blaming others or circumstances, criticizing things because they are not perfect, demanding that we solve every problem, etc."[3] Celebrating joy is a choice that you can make.

You have choices to make:

Do you choose to suffer, or do you choose joy?

Do you want to hang on to pain or take the risk and live with jubilance?

Do you choose to stick with old habits, or are you ready to take the risk and live joyously?

From what we know about neuroplasticity, you can rewire or change your brain at any age just by thinking differently. You are the architect and builder of your own brain, continually altering its structure, cell number, circuitry, and chemistry. These alterations are a direct result of everything you do, experience, think, and believe.

The Greatest Expression of You process is a purposeful and disciplined practice to create the changes in your life you want by thinking differently and rewiring your brain. To change your thoughts, emotions, and behaviors requires intentional focused thought coupled with genuine emotion.

It's not enough to simply state or think about the change you desire once and expect that change to happen. For lasting physical, mental, and emotional changes to occur, you must affirm your desires repeatedly and with enough emotion (joy) so that the new way of being hardwires, overriding old thoughts and emotions that are no longer useful.

---

[3] *The Journal of Christian Healing,* Volume 19, #2, Summer, 1997, pp. 3–19.

Those of us who were alive when President Kennedy, Martin Luther King Jr., and Robert Kennedy were assassinated remember where we were when we first heard the news. More recently, we remember where we were and what we were doing the morning of September 11, 2001, when two planes struck the Twin Towers of the World Trade Center.

When trauma occurs, neurons fire together and wire together. Traumatic events need only happen once to become hardwired. Most of us have no recollection of what we were doing on April 10, 2010. I don't even know what day of the week it was. I have no memory or emotion attached to that date, so there is no hardwiring.

Trauma is not limited to huge life events. Trauma can occur at three years of age, tripping on a blade of grass and scraping your knee. Grandma picks you up, kisses the boo-boo, wipes the tears away, and gives you a hug and a homemade chocolate chip cookie.

This is when the hardwiring happens. Pain is followed by unconditional love, safety, and protection. These are then coupled with feel-good chocolate, fat, flour, and sugar that hit the same opiate receptors as heroin. Years later, when trauma occurs again, Grandma is no longer around to pick you up and give you a hug, but chocolate chip cookies are readily available.

At the age of three, Grandma's hugs and a cookie worked, and your unconscious mind latched on to these remedies to protect you in the future. Today, however, all those cookies can make you fat and sick.

In Chapter 3, I told you that you can write a new story for living your life. Joy is an essential ingredient for your new life story. Just think the difference you would experience in your life if you lived each day joyfully! Your subconscious mind reacts to emotion more than anything else. When people perfunctorily say affirmations or apathetically express their dreams for the future, the subconscious mind will not pay attention and take action. Your subconscious does not care about anything unless it makes you feel either good or bad.

What Is Joy?

What is joy, anyway? *The Oxford Dictionary* defines joy as "a feeling of great pleasure and happiness." It's been said that "Happiness is an emotion in which we experience feelings ranging from contentment and satisfaction to bliss and intense pleasure," whereas joy "Is a stronger, less common feeling than happiness." [4]

Other terms for joy are *delight, gaiety,* and *bliss*. My favorite description of joy comes from Theopedia, which describes joy as, "A state of mind and an orientation of the heart. It is a settled state of contentment, confidence, and hope."[5] Joy plays a profound role in creating deep shifts.

The Oxford Companion to Emotion and the Affective Sciences defines joy as a "Pleasant state that shares conceptual space with other positive emotions such as gladness, elation, happiness, and, to a lesser extent, amusement." It goes on to say that "Phenomenologically, joy feels bright and light. Colors seem more vivid. Physical movements become more fluid. Smiles

[4] Agarwal, Shubhi, "Is there a difference between Happiness and Joy?" (2021) Retrieved from:
https://www.researchgate.net/post/Is_there_a_difference_between_Happiness_and_Joy2/5ff6ee5c0e07c508e61bdf47/citation/download.
[5] https://www.theopedia.com/joy

become difficult to suppress. Joy broadens people's attention and thinking.[6]"

Joy brings feelings of ease, freedom, and safety, and it enhances resilience to future obstacles or threats. Joy enriches learning. When you *en*joy, you are *in*-joy!

When I ask people about the most joyful time in their life, some must reflect for a bit, and others start sharing immediately. The sparkle in their eyes, the ear-to-ear smile, the rose color that comes to their face, and the enthusiasm I hear in their voices are all clear signs that they have joy.

Matthew started telling me about hiking in the mountains and being on top of the world. He described experiencing a calm, loosening breath in his chest and a sense of being at One.

Shirlee went right to her wedding day when she and her wife were dancing with their fathers. She portrayed this as her chest opening to love.

For Emma, she found joy in the hugs of her daughters and experienced warmth in her chest.

And for Arash, he described a tingling in his chest and the awe he felt at the birth of his son.

My most joyful times include the amalgamation of the births of my son and granddaughters, walking hand in hand on Maalaea Beach with my wife, gardening with my granddaughter, Ellie, Luna's puppy breath, standing on top of Mount Rainier, boating on the Mississippi River, and riding my bike down Baker Hill.

---

[6] *The Oxford Companion to Emotion and Affective Sciences* **quoted in** Johnson, Matthew Kuan "Joy: a review of the literature and suggestions for future directions"
https://www.tandfonline.com/doi/full/10.1080/17439760.2019.1685581

Any one of these brings me joy, but when I meld them together, the culminating joy is powerful!

I love to laugh

I can't imagine joy without laughter. So, it makes sense that one of my all-time favorite movies is *Mary Poppins*. Several mornings each week, I start my day watching the "I Love to Laugh" scene from *Mary Poppins*. This song becomes an earworm throughout my day that brings a smile to my face, joy to my heart, and lifts my soul to sing.

The words to the second verse are:

"The more I laugh, the more I fill with glee
And the more the glee
The more I'm a merrier me, it's embarrassing
The more I'm a merrier me.[7]"

One of my goals in every client session is to make sure that we share a smile and a laugh. Even when I am with someone who just lost a loved one, I ask them to tell me their favorite funny story about the person or pet that died. Why? Because laughter is healing.

Dr. Joel Goodman, founder of The HUMOR Project, tells us that one of his patients created:

L A U G H T E R is an acronym for:

Love And Understanding Give Hope Toward Emotional Recovery

I love that, and it is so true.

---

[7] Composed by Richard M. Sherman and Robert B. Sherman, Walt Disney's *Mary Poppins*, 1964.

According to the Mayo Clinic, whether you're laughing at a sitcom on TV, a humorous video on YouTube, or quietly giggling at a newspaper cartoon, laughing does you good. Laughter is a great form of stress relief.

When you laugh, it doesn't just lighten your load mentally. It actually induces physical changes in your body such as stimulating your heart, lungs and muscles, and increases the endorphins that are released by your brain.

Laughter can also activate and relieve your stress response and stimulate circulation, and aid muscle relaxation.

Long-term laughter can improve your immune system, ease pain by causing the body to produce its own natural painkillers, lessen depression and anxiety, and may make you feel happier. [8]

Laughter stimulates the creative part of our brain, helping with problem-solving and can boost mental alertness and memory

There was research at the University of Tsukuba in Japan where they studied a group of diabetics. The researchers took fasting blood sugar levels of the study's participants and then fed them a meal. Rather than giving the participants their diabetes medication, they had them watch a comedy for sixty minutes, and then again, the researchers checked the participants' blood sugars. Every time the participants' blood sugar was within healthy normal limits.

I encourage you to start each day with a laugh. You can watch a funny video on YouTube or other social media, go online and

---

[8] Mayo Clinic, "Stress relief from laughter? It's no joke!" 2021 https://www.mayoclinic.org/healthy-lifestyle/stress-management/in-depth/stress-relief/art-20044456

learn a new joke and share it with your family. You will find many laughter yoga and laughter therapy videos on YouTube, and you can learn laughter exercises that you can do on your own. Allow your laughter to be spontaneous and infectious.

Laughter truly is the best medicine. Go ahead and give it a try. Turn the corners of your mouth up into a smile and then give a laugh even if it feels a little forced. Once you've laughed, notice how you're feeling. Are your muscles a little less tense, and do you feel more relaxed? That's the natural wonder of laughing.

Laughter can get you out of your head and into a more positive state. Giving yourself permission to laugh out loud at nothing is incredibly freeing!

Laughter can enhance the quality of your experiences and can help you to realign with joy. Laughter is joyful and expands the energies of the Greatest Expression of You.

The Power of Joy

In 1979, Harvard Psychologist Ellen Langer conducted a fascinating study involving nursing home residents that I believe demonstrates the power of joy. The purpose of this study was to see if, when people are in a psychologically better setting—one they would associate with a better, younger version of themselves—their bodies might follow along. "Wherever you put the mind, you're necessarily putting the body," Langer explained.

According to an article in *The New York Times Magazine*, Bruce Grierson wrote that "Eight men in their seventies stepped out of a van in front of a converted monastery in New Hampshire. They shuffled forward, a few of them arthritically stooped, a couple with canes. Then they passed through the door and entered a time warp. Perry Como crooned on a vintage radio. Ed Sullivan welcomed guests on a black-and-white TV. Everything inside—including the books on the shelves and the magazines lying around—were designed to conjure 1959.[9]"

The men in this group didn't just reminisce about what things were like at that time. They were instructed to behave as if it were actually 1959. In this study, there was also a control group that was instructed to merely reminisce about their lives twenty years earlier in 1959.

In her book, *Counterclockwise,* Langer wrote that a week later, both the control group and the experimental group showed improvements in "physical strength, manual dexterity, gait, posture, perception, memory, cognition, taste sensitivity, hearing, and vision." [10]

As part of the study, four independent volunteers, who knew nothing about the study, looked at before and after photos of the men in the experimental group and perceived those in the "after" photos as an average of two years younger than those in the "before."

According to Langer, on the last day of the study, men "who had seemed so frail" just days before ended up playing "an impromptu touch football game on the front lawn." Personally, I would have loved to have been there to watch the transformation of these men. The thought of these frail men

[9] Grierson, Bruce, "What if Age Is Nothing but a Mind-Set?," *The New York Times Magazine*, October 22, 2014, https://www.nytimes.com/2014/10/26/magazine/what-if-age-is-nothing-but-a-mind-set.html?_r=0.
[10] Ellen J. Langer, *Counterclockwise*: Mindful Health and the Power of Possibility, Ballantine Books, May 19, 2009

playing touch football gives me great joy, and it even makes me feel younger thinking about it.

So, I ask you, what do you think can change in your life when you decide to live each moment of your life *in*-joy?

Your Turn for Joy

Take a moment now and take three deep, relaxing breaths in through your nose and let them out through your mouth. Bring your breath deep into the center point of your body: about three fingers below your navel and midway between your front and back.

On the last breath, imagine bringing your breath all the way from your center point into your head. Fill your head with the breath, and then let it out through your mouth. Now, reflect on a time or times in your life when you experienced the greatest joy.

Was it the first kiss with your sweetheart? Was it the first dance at your wedding? Was it the birth of a child? Was it holding your new puppy and smelling that sweet puppy breath? Were you skiing down a mountain or standing on its peak? Is it spending time with your grandchildren? Maybe you were flying a kite or riding your bike.

Immerse yourself in this time of joy and allow yourself to appreciate the experience. Where do you feel the joy in your body? What physical sensation(s) are you experiencing? Does the joy radiate from your heart, your chest, or somewhere else in your body?

Let yourself totally experience your joy with all your senses. What do you see and hear? What do you smell and taste? What do you feel, both internally and externally? What is the physical sensation of joy in your body?

Now memorize this joy and how it feels and where you feel it. Remember this joy and the physical sensations so that you have it as a future resource. When you are memorizing joy, do so enthusiastically! I've learned about the importance of enthusiasm from my clients. I've always known that client sessions, both in my offices and online, are the best classrooms for my own learning. I love that I learn from each client session.

Bob shared with me about how his relationship with his wife has transformed from one of bickering, hurt, and disappointment to one of love and caring. How did he do that? By using the **Greatest Expression of You** process that I teach to all clients.

With joy and excitement in his voice, Bob shared with me about how he uses the process throughout the day, and twice he used the word *enthusiasm*. From mentally rehearsing being his **Greatest Expression** to using self-hypnosis to remind himself of who he is becoming, Bob made it clear that he's enthusiastic about every aspect of the process.

His choice of words caught my attention; his joy and enthusiasm were captivating. I realized that enthusiasm is another powerful component of joy that helps wire new neurons together. Doing so, you can create stronger neurological connections to being the **Greatest Expression of You**.

Putting Joy to Use

Remember when I asked you at the beginning of this chapter to recall an upsetting event? You did that easily because the experiences with the strongest emotional content become more hardwired. Let's do that again. This may seem unexpected, perhaps even unpleasant, but try something with me: think for a moment of a trauma in your life. What do you see and hear? What do you feel, smell, and taste? What do you feel, internally and externally? Notice the shift in your body, thoughts, and emotions now that you are no longer focused on being joyful.

Now, remember joy. Bring joy to mind and allow yourself to truly appreciate it. Where do you feel the joy in your body? What physical sensation(s) are you experiencing? Does the joy radiate from your heart or chest?

Let yourself totally experience your joy with all your senses. What do you see and hear? What do you smell and taste? What do you feel, both internally and externally? What is the physical sensation of joy in your body?

Remember how this joy feels and where you feel it.

Notice how quickly you can switch from the trauma to being joyful. Remember this. As soon as you become aware of upset, you can flip the switch to being joyful. Your thoughts, emotions, and physical sensations can act as an alarm or smoke detector or even sound off the famed alert: "Danger, Will Robinson, danger!"

Each can warn you when you are slipping back into old habits and ways of being. As soon as you become aware of the alarm, remember joy. Feel your joy radiating through every cell of your body. Imagine how different your life can be!

Grieving Joy

In a phone session, Fridoline described her most joyful time in life as a young woman in Europe. Her extended family would gather at the family cottage in the mountains on weekends. They played games, hiked, sang, danced, and shared luscious meals. When I heard the deep joy in her voice, I stopped her and helped her connect to the thoughts, emotions, and sensations in her body so that she could memorize this joy. She giggled with elation at first, then went silent and started to cry. Fridoline was experiencing melancholy joy by grieving the loss of most of these family members and the times they had shared sixty years ago.

We talked for a moment so that she could acknowledge the grief, and she then easily returned to joy. Fridoline's goal for hypnosis was to overcome grief, depression, and anxiety. Grief was hardwired and familiar. Joy was a novel experience for her, and she quickly slipped back into her old habit of grieving.

I explained to Fridoline that she can be joyous and still feel sad that most of these family members had died and that these wonderful weekends were no longer possible. I reminded her that she can forever experience the joy of these memories.

Living in joy is not Pollyanna-ish thinking, and it certainly isn't about denying anger, hurt, fear, sadness, or trauma. You can live with the duality of joy while acknowledging loss. When you are mindful and live in joy, you can walk peacefully with the past.

If you find yourself slipping out of joy and into the loss of that experience, take a breath, acknowledge the loss, and return to joy.

Addicted to Joy

When I checked in with Susie to see how she was doing, she responded to me by exclaiming, "Today, I would tell you that I am addicted to joy!"

One year previously, Susie was suffering with anxiety. She was making herself sick, she was depressed, and she was struggling in her leadership role at Amazon. To top it off, her relationship was suffering as well.

Meeting eight times over three months, I taught Susie to use self-hypnosis, the **Greatest Expression of You** process, and mindfulness-based stress reduction techniques. From our first session, Susie understood that she was addicted to and perpetuating anxiety. Thanks to the healing hypnosis therapy that I used, she was able to let go of the past. She also came to understand that the past isn't happening now and that she can write a new story based on this moment.

When we first met, Susie had memorized anxiety. The thoughts and emotions she experienced were based on past events, not on her life in the present moment. Her anxiety produced the highly addictive fight-or-flight response chemicals, catecholamine hormones, including epinephrine and norepinephrine, which prepare muscles for violent action.

Today, Susie is calm and relaxed. She has been promoted at work, and her relationship is filled with love. Susie learned that she could live *in*-joy and no longer needs anxiety. Instead, thoughts and emotions of joy produce endorphins, serotonin, dopamine, and oxytocin—all feel-good chemicals—and release into her body. Today, Susie is addicted to joy!

For a variety of reasons, some people really struggle to remember a time when they experienced joy. As a result, they grapple with recreating the thoughts, memories, emotions, and sensations of joy. With their permission, I guide them on a safe journey so that they can find and memorize joy. If you are one of these people and would like my help, please call or email me.

Chapter 6

Mental Rehearsal

"Excellence is an art won by training and habituation. We do not act rightly because we have virtue or excellence, but we rather have those because we have acted rightly. We are what we repeatedly do. Excellence, then, is not an act but a habit."
—Aristotle, Greek critic, philosopher, physicist, and zoologist (384 BC–322 BC)

Mental Rehearsal is the training and habituation of being your Best Self. It is an important and powerful component to the **Greatest Expression of You** process. Aristotle tells us we develop a talent for the things we repeatedly practice. Too often, we repeatedly rehearse negativity and failure, which results in successfully achieving negativity and failure. Mental Rehearsal of the **Greatest Expression of You** lets you choose your thoughts, emotions, and actions wisely. This helps you achieve excellence in what really matters to you.

Mental Rehearsal is a step-by-step thought process used to mentally practice being the **Greatest Expression of You** throughout your day. It is a plan that you make in your mind to prime your brain for action.

One client referred to Mental Rehearsal as a *walk-through*. In the theatre world, a walk-through is a rough rehearsal of a play, film, or other performance without an audience or cameras present. People in the tech industry will tell you that a walk-through is a software model of a building or other object in which the user can simulate walking around.

Merriam-Webster defines walk-through as:

"An activity in which someone walks through an area, building, etc., in order to inspect it; the act of going slowly through the steps of a process, job, etc., in order to practice doing it or to help someone learn it; an explanation or guide that tells you how to do something by explaining each of its parts or steps."

When Kathy, an Amazon employee, first heard about Mental Rehearsal, her face lit up. "Oh, project planning!" she said. "Just like I plan a project at work, I'll plan how to be my Best Self each day." Kathy went on to say that just like at Amazon, the Mental Rehearsal is much more about outcome than it is about output.

For the purposes of the **Greatest Expression of You**, Mental Rehearsal is the act of mentally rehearsing joyfully being your Best Self throughout your upcoming day. Mentally rehearsing an upcoming meeting or potentially difficult conversation is also advantageous. Mental Rehearsal is project planning. It is training and habituation, and of course, it includes a positive outcome.

Let me begin by talking about Mental Rehearsal versus imagination:

Imagination:

If I imagine getting ready to go to Maui, I picture myself getting T-shirts off the shelf, swimsuits out of the drawer, my flip-flops off the floor, and maybe a pair of blue jeans to bring on the plane. I will not need any other long pants because most of my time will be spent rotating on the beach, boogie boarding, bodysurfing, and snorkeling. One night I might rent dive equipment and go to Black Sand Beach for a night dive through the lava tube and check out the sharks.

Wait, what happened to getting ready to go to Maui? I went from swimsuits to swimming with sharks and never finished packing. I got lost in my imagination, recalling one of my favorite Maui night dives. Imagination takes us to far-off places, and we forget what our real objective is all about.

Mental Rehearsal:

Unlike imagination, Mental Rehearsal is goal-directed. Here is my Mental Rehearsal for getting ready to go to Maui:

I get the suitcases from the garage and bring them into the house. I grab T-shirts from the shelf, underwear from the top drawer, swimsuits from another drawer, and shorts from another. I retrieve my flip-flops from the corner of the closet. From my office, I gather phone cords, chargers, my iPad, and my phone. In my bathroom, I gather my razor, toothbrush, toothpaste, shampoo, deodorant, and other toiletries. Finally, I enter the kitchen and bag enough oatmeal for my trip.

This is a step-by-step plan I make in my mind so that when it is time to pack, my brain is primed, and my body will easily flow with the plan. I have already laid the groundwork: the neuropathways.

To *Mentally Rehearse being the **Greatest Expression of You,*** begin by reading your two or three sentences that describe being the ***Greatest Expression of You.***

Now, Mentally Rehearse joyfully being the **Greatest Expression of You** throughout the day. Be sure to give thanks for being the **Greatest Expression of You** because living in a state of gratitude is living in a state of receivership. (I will talk more about gratitude in Chapter 9.)

As you Mentally Rehearse being the **Greatest Expression of You**, consider the following:

How do you live?
How do you think?
How do you talk?
How do you act?
How do you love?
What emotions are present?
What does it feel like to be the **Greatest Expression of You**?

Be sure that an important component of your Mental Rehearsal is being joyful. Include as much positive emotion as you can possibly invoke.

Mentally Rehearse Your Day

One of the first things that I do each morning as I brush my teeth is to Mentally Rehearse my day. I begin by recalling Joy. I feel its warm glow in my heart and chest as I walk through the anticipated events of my day. I also Mentally Rehearse being my Best Self for unexpected experiences that may occur. In my mind, this is like watching a movie in fast-forward. One of the many amazing things about your brain is that with its one hundred billion neurons, it can generate and act on a given thought in less than one hundred and fifty milliseconds. You can think of this Mental Rehearsal as a time-lapse movie, like when you watch a flower blossom open in a very few moments.

Sometimes my Mental Rehearsal lasts for a minute, and other times the process takes longer. Throughout the day, I mentally rehearse for several events; I walk through my next client session, a bike ride that I am about to begin, and the act of writing the next section of this book.

Mentally Rehearsing riding my bike is an example of Mental Rehearsal that involves both *Being* and *Doing*. My Beingness is joyful and fun. The Doing is rehearsing the physical act of riding: my upper body relaxed, shoulders down, hands relaxed, breath steady and calm, my legs powerful pistons. I am alert for traffic and road hazards. While I ride through a curve, I look where I want to go, my eyes on the road's horizon. As I corner, I shift my weight and lean the bike into the curve with my inside knee turning out. Throughout this rehearsal, I ride with confidence, strength, energy, and stamina, making sure I return home safely and hang my bike in the garage.

This mental planning of events creates neuropathways in my brain so that as I ride, I already have the road map for success.

(A note on returning home safely: I find that too often, people do not carry their goals, their life's vision, and their Mental Rehearsal to the conclusion. When I trained to climb Mount Rainier, I was taught that the goal is not to climb the mountain; the goal is to return home safely! After being taught how to tie a Prusik knot, I Mentally Rehearsed successfully tying the knot multiple times. By the day of our ascent, I was able to do it with my eyelids closed. Fortunately, no one from our team fell into a crevasse and had to be rescued. But when we jumped across small crevasses or walked on a ladder across a bigger one, it sure helped with the confidence knowing that I had the training to get back out.)

Sometimes, life provides opportunities that were not part of any Mental Rehearsal. While riding my bike in August 2019, I was hit by a car which totaled my bike and left me and my body bruised and sore. The temptation to wallow in self-pity was strong, but I kept focusing on being the guy that Luna thinks I am and remembering Joy.

As a result of this accident, in July 2020, I had rotator cuff surgery. Before and after the surgery, I Mentally Rehearsed optimal blood flow in my shoulder pre-surgery, minimal blood flow during surgery, and optimal flow post-surgery. I asked my unconscious mind to produce the right amount of collagen to promote healing. During the weeks of physical therapy, I Mentally Rehearsed my range of motion, safely lifting weights, and strengthening my arms, shoulders, back, and abs.

Your Turn

For fun, try this: If you can, stand up and hold one arm out in front of you and point your index finger straight ahead. (If you can't safely stand, stay seated, preferably on the edge of your bed or in a chair with a low back, and do this exercise). Now, keep your feet grounded on the floor, pointed ahead of you. Turn your upper body as far as you can and note how far behind you can point with your finger. Return to facing forward.

Now close your eyelids and Mentally Rehearse being able to turn your upper body 360 degrees. Next, with your eyelids open, hold your arm and finger out in front of you again. Turn your upper body and see how much further you can turn. Pretty amazing, huh?

Mental Rehearsal is much like practicing for a sport, performance, or musical instrument. Sports teams practice on and off the field between games. Actors go to rehearsals.

Orchestras rehearse for upcoming performances. Students practice the piano between lessons. (If only I had practiced!)

When you Mentally Rehearse, your brain rewires itself to your wishes, and your body is reconditioned to prepare itself for that upcoming event. Just like the piano study in Chapter 3, your body responds as if you are practicing the event. Your brain does not know the difference between mental or physical effort. For example, do you remember when, in Chapter 3, I asked you to imagine biting into a lemon? Have you ever been in a theatre when one person coughs, and soon you are coughing? And every time I think about when one of my granddaughters came home from school with head lice, my head starts to itch.

Other common examples of mind-body responses include blushing, yawning, and even erections! All of these are very real unconscious responses to external stimuli. This response to external stimuli is very real. When you intentionally Mentally Rehearse an activity or your day, combined with powerful emotion, you are supercharging your brain and your body's ability to perform.

Have You Been Mentally Rehearsing the Wrong Thing?

Reflect on this for a moment:

What do you Mentally Rehearse as you brush your teeth in the morning? Do you worry about being able to get to work on time, a potentially difficult meeting or encounter, or some other challenge you are facing? How do you imagine dealing with these things? Are you Mentally Rehearsing them going well? Or, as I hear from many clients, are you rehearsing what you do not want? What are you thinking about and finally demonstrating? Are you living in fear and imagining the worst? Do you Mentally

Rehearse negative future fantasies? If you still have a pulse, the answer to these four questions is most likely "Yes."

Studies show that we have anywhere from six thousand to sixty thousand thoughts per day, and about 80 percent of these thoughts are "negative." Negative thoughts are a normal part of human functioning, so don't be alarmed about having them. The good news is that you don't have to believe those negative thoughts—you do have a choice! That's where growth lies—when you acknowledge a negative thought without believing it. And the more you do this, the less "negative thoughts" you have and the easier it is to recognize them when you do have them.

Here is another question for you: How often do the things you fear happen? Not very often, right? As we covered in Chapter 2, 85 percent of what you fear and worry about does not happen. Your track record of awfulizing has a high rate of "*didn't happen.*" Even when those negative future fantasies don't happen, your body still responds as if they are happening. If you are imagining you are being chased by a saber-toothed tiger, your body produces the exact same fear chemicals as if you were being chased by that saber-toothed tiger. Whatever you mentally attend to is what you are and what you will become. This is the Law of Attention. Living in a constant state of fear, stress, and anxiety is hazardous to your health as you become whatever you mentally attend to. It's like you are praying for bad things to happen!

On YouTube, there is a short clip from a Frasier episode titled, "Frasier and Niles Learn How to Ride a Bike." Frasier keeps focusing on the tree and repeatedly runs into the tree on the bike. He exclaims, "It's that damn sycamore. It's got a magnetic hold on me." Daphne replies, "That's because you keep focusing on it. Whatever you do, put it out of your mind. The more you think about it, the worse it gets." When Niles tells Frasier that he's a cloud scuttling across a clear blue sky, Frasier focuses on the cloud and rides the bike past the tree.

Whether you affirm your thoughts consciously or unconsciously makes no difference. What you mentally attend to is what you are and what you will become. Your attention brings your thoughts to life and makes real what was essentially unreal. If you focus on physical pain in your body, the circuits that perceive pain in the brain become electrically activated, causing pain. When you direct your awareness to something other than pain, such as Joy, you turn off the brain circuits that process pain and bodily sensations, and the pain goes away.

From this moment forward, what will you attend to? Will your story be about negativity, fear, and anger? Or is your new story about love and peace of mind? Will you think about how you will fail or about how you will succeed? Will you create negative or positive future fantasies? You have a choice. You have the power to write your new story.

Over the years, people have told me they just did not think they could change. "This is the way I've always been," they say. "You can't teach an old dog new tricks."

We now know that this is not true. Neuroplasticity is your brain's ability to change its synaptic wiring by learning information and recording experiences. You can do this at any age—you are never too old to be a better version of you.

Feedback from Real Clients

I love receiving emails from people telling me how they use Mental Rehearsal in their daily life. I received an email from Amanda who wrote:

"Roger, it's been almost a year since our last session, but I wanted to write and tell you how grateful Jon and I are that we found you.

Three years ago, when I first called you, I thought our marriage of seventeen years was over. Thanks to you, we just celebrated our twentieth anniversary!

My husband and I both love and use the **Greatest Expression of You**, and our favorite part of it is the Mental Rehearsal. For many years in our marriage, we both mentally rehearsed our hurt and anger and how we were going to get even. Jon could come in in a good mood, but I had worked myself up into such a frenzy that before he could say 'Hi,' I'd be yelling at him about what he did wrong, and a fight would ensue.

Now, we are quite different. Before he comes into the house, we both remember the joy we felt when we first met and at our wedding, and then I mentally rehearse having open, loving, honest conversations with him. When we sit down to talk about our finances, we each remember our Joy and then Mentally Rehearse, listening with love and honesty so that we both feel heard and so that we reach agreements that we both feel good about. Before, when we were together, we fought, and now our anger and resentment have been replaced with love, laughter, and smiles. Our marriage and love have never been stronger. My only regret is that we didn't learn this twenty years ago in our premarital counseling.

With love and gratitude, Amanda."

Amanda's email is an example of what can happen when you take the time out of your busy schedule to intentionally dream a new reality. By doing so, your brain rewires itself so you can create your future to be greater than your past.

People who use Mental Rehearsal every day tell me that they are calmer, more confident, and happier than they were prior to our first session together.

Master Mind

When we lived on Bainbridge Island, I volunteered as a sports psychology coach with the Bainbridge Boys Lacrosse team for several years. One night, I met with the guys in the locker room before a game and overheard one of the teammates mention Napoleon Hill's famed book, *Think and Grow Rich*. I asked why they were talking about Napoleon Hill, and it turned out another coach had bought them each a copy. Much to my delighted surprise, they were reading it!

I called the boys together, and I told them about Napoleon Hill's Master Mind process. From then on, the team divided into groups of two before games and practices to do Master Mind together.

My experience with the lacrosse team led me to think of Mental Rehearsal as a Master Mind process. In the 1920s and 30s, Napoleon Hill wrote the books, *The Law of Success* and *Think and Grow Rich*. He introduced the concept of "master mind alliance."

Hill described the master mind alliance as "The coordination of knowledge and effort of two or more people, who work toward a definite purpose in the spirit of harmony." He went on to write, "No two minds ever come together without thereby creating a third, invisible, intangible force, which may be likened to a third mind [the master mind]."

While the Mental Rehearsal process does not include another person, it does involve consciously and purposefully directing your thoughts. Through this process, you fire and wire new neurons together. On a fundamental level, you train your body to be Your Best Self. In turn, your body believes you are Your Best Self, and you can and do act accordingly.

Napoleon Hill might tell us that Mental Rehearsal is the coordination of your mind and your body coming together in a spirit of harmony, thereby creating a third, powerful force—the Master Mind.

Life Happens

A client and I were discussing the **Greatest Expression of You** process, and he asked an important question. "What should I do when I've mentally rehearsed the events of the day, but then life happens and messes with my plans?"

I was reminded of the adage, "If you want to make God laugh, tell Him your plans." When you are being your Greatest Expression and life does not go according to plans, adjust, and move on.

There are few things in life that you can control. You cannot control the weather, other people, traffic, or most other events. Being the **Greatest Expression of You** gives you the power to be in control of your own thoughts, emotions, and behavior.

If you are being the **Greatest Expression of You**, you learn to roll with the punches of daily life.

Chapter 7

Meditate

"Meditation will not carry you to another world, but it will reveal the most profound and awesome dimensions of the world in which you already live. Calmly contemplating these dimensions and bringing them into the service of compassion and kindness is the right way to make rapid gains in meditation as well as in life."
—Zen Master Hsing Yun

"Your goal is not to battle with the mind, but to witness the mind."
—Swami Muktananda

I hope by now you have written your **Greatest Expression of You**. I also hope you are focusing on memorizing Joy and getting better and better at Mentally Rehearsing being your Best Self. Meditation will help bring these all together.

There are many types of meditation, ranging from the Zazen practice of emptying your mind to other practices in which you train your mind to look within, to ponder, focus, and redirect your thoughts. Meditation has been called the "art of doing nothing." While the benefits of meditation have been scientifically proven, there are so many differing views on what meditation actually is and how to do it that the word doesn't mean anything. There is no word in the English language that can exactly describe the actual practice of meditation, so if you find yourself confused about what meditation means, that's okay. Letting go of the attachment to the definition of meditation is one of the first steps in meditating.

Throughout my life, I have pursued the perfect place for meditation and the perfect form of meditation. I meditated in church and in beautiful cathedrals. I attended Zen meditation centers, walking meditations on labyrinths. I've meditated on mountaintops, on tropical beaches, in front of campfires, and in my own backyard. And I've attended meditation classes and read many books. I love meditation, but what I have come to realize is that brief active mindfulness meditation sessions are best for me. I can do it quietly or actively in the moment no matter where I am, which makes it perfect for the Greatest Expression of You.

I like to think of mindfulness meditation as a gym workout for my brain. Active mindfulness meditation is a state of awareness that allows you to make sense of what is happening to you. It is constancy, a capacity to be with what is true moment after moment. Mindfulness meditation is a way of using a detached perspective to evaluate your own behavior and attitudes to detect where you are being less than your best self, expand your perspective, and detach from your current mindset and beliefs. This opens you to Becoming the Greatest Expression of You so that you can create your future to be greater than your past. So, from this point forward, when I use the word "Meditation," I am referring to active, mindful Meditation.

Meditation is a way to focus your thoughts. It can help you to contemplate, plan, or project being your Best Self. I like the *Cambridge Dictionary's* definition of meditation as it is perfect for the implementation of the **Greatest Expression of You**:

"The act of giving your attention to only one thing, either as a religious activity or as a way of becoming calm and relaxed," and "serious thought or study, or the product of this activity." [11]

When you mindfully meditate, you have the opportunity to recognize your passing thoughts, feelings, and sensory reactions without judgment. You are simply sitting with and acknowledging what's happening in your mind and body.

In his book *The Genie in Your Genes,* Dawson Church quotes Dr. Robert Dozor, "Meditation—all by itself—may offer more to the health of a modern American than all the pharmaceutical remedies put together."[12]

The list of physical, mental, and emotional health benefits of meditation is long. Here are just a few:

Helps reduce stress
Controls anxiety
Promotes emotional health
Fosters kindness and happiness
Increases attention span
Helps with pain control
Enhances self-awareness
Helps reduce memory loss
Improves sleep
Lowers blood pressure

[11] "MEDITATION: Definition in the *Cambridge Dictionary*." dictionary.cambridge.org/us/dictionary/english/meditation.
[12] Dr. Robert Dozor **quoted in** Dawson Church, Ph.D. *The Genie in Your Genes*. Elite Books. Kindle Edition, 2009.

Circadian Rhythm

We can take advantage of what nature has built into us—a rhythmic cycle of activity and rest. Many people are familiar with the Circadian Cycle, which regulates our sleep patterns, but another interesting rhythm within us is the Ultradian Rhythm.

In our modern, high-paced culture, productivity is of great value. When we need to take a break, signals such as loss of focus, or hunger, thirst, and restlessness are often ignored, and instead, people reach out for artificial ways to stay on point, including caffeine and unhealthy foods. The body then begins to draw on stress hormones to help, which sustains being in sympathetic nervous system arousal. In turn, this response wears on the natural capacity to self-regulate body functions and emotions. In the fight-or-flight response, one is less able to think objectively and begins to react rather than respond to life.

And, even worse, due to the conditioned wiring of such states, when people don't have to be working, they fail to allow themselves to really relax!

To operate at our best, it is necessary to take a break about every ninety minutes or so. The conscious mind will actually do this often below our awareness. Think of the times when you noticed that you had "spaced out" or caught yourself daydreaming.

Ernest Rossi has conducted a lot of research on this topic and coined the phrase, "The Ultradian Healing Response." He prescribed a twenty-minute break every ninety minutes or so to recharge the mind and body. For people whose lives are just too busy to afford a twenty-minute break, inserting brief recesses periodically during the day can achieve similar positive results.

If Meditation Were a Drug

I once read that if meditation were a drug, it would be medical malpractice for your doctor to fail to prescribe it. Meditation benefits every system in your body, measurably improving your body's ability to resist disease.

Studies show that in addition to making you calmer, meditation significantly elevates levels of antibodies and blood cells which are associated with increased immune function. When you meditate, you improve your body's ability to resist disease and the effects of stress, and blood flow to your heart muscles increases. Around the world, researchers continue to study the benefits of meditation on many diseases.

Dean Ornish, MD asks, "How did we get to a point in medicine where interventions such as radioactive stents, coronary angioplasty, and bypass surgery are considered conventional, whereas eating vegetables, walking, meditating, and participating in support groups are considered radical?"

With the power of meditation, you direct your brain to provide your body with the healing chemicals it needs. Unlike prescription drugs, the neurochemicals secreted by your brain during meditation are free and do not have a long list of side effects.

Studies indicate that the practice of meditation activates neural structures involved in attention and control of the autonomic nervous system. Meditation increases your melatonin production, which helps you sleep better and reduces the severity of cancer. Meditation protects and lengthens telomeres to help protect your chromosomes. Well-protected chromosomes create vibrant cells, which contribute to vitality and health.

Using meditation, you flood your body with hormones that support health and happiness. During meditation, your heart rate, blood pressure, and muscular tension decrease in tandem with stress hormones such as cortisol and adrenaline. You already know that chronic anxiety, depression, and anger are harmful to your health.

Meditation increases mindfulness, which leads to making healthier lifestyle choices. With regular meditation, you decrease your chances of disease and increase the prospects for ease in your life.

Other benefits of meditation include reduced incidence of strokes, heart disease, and cancer. It improves resting heart rate, lowers blood pressure, diminishes chronic pain, and reduces anxiety and depression.

The benefits of meditation do not end when your meditation session ends. Meditation can help carry you more calmly through your day and may help you manage symptoms of certain medical conditions.

It has been said that meditation and hypnosis are the steroids of relaxation. Hypnosis and meditation build up the portion of your brain that produces happiness. In the next chapter, we will cover self-hypnosis in depth, and you will learn how to hypnotize yourself.

How to Meditate

What should meditation look like? Ultimately, how you meditate is up to you and what you are able and willing to do. If you have the time and the dexterity, meditation can certainly involve spending thirty to sixty minutes in the lotus position. For most of us, that is not our reality. Your meditation on Being the **Greatest Expression of You** can be quick and easy.

It is important that skills like meditation be easy and practical. I suggest you post your **Greatest Expression** on your bathroom mirror and read it first thing each morning. Next, remember and memorize Joy and Mentally Rehearse being your Best Self. Finally, meditate (think, reflect, concentrate, contemplate) on being your Best Self as you go about your morning routine of brushing your teeth, washing your face, taking a shower, and so on. The more you focus your attention on your meditation during this time, the greater your benefits will be.

As you meditate on your **Greatest Expression**, see, feel, and hear what it is like to be your greatest self physically, mentally, emotionally, and spiritually. Being the **Greatest Expression of You**, how do you live? How do you love? How do you act? How do you think? How do you feel? How are you *being* in this world? Remember how sometimes you get totally lost in thought as you brush your teeth? Take control, direct your thoughts, and allow yourself to be totally absorbed in your meditation. The intent of meditation is to nurture those states of mind that are beneficial to peace and well-being and to eliminate those that are not.

You may notice your mind wander during meditation. As soon as you become aware, there is no need to judge. Simply acknowledge that there is a thought and bring your attention to your breath. Breathe in and breathe out. It is natural for your mind to wander. Be gentle with yourself when you realize your thoughts are roaming again. Ultimately, your goal is to become more mindful and live more in the present moment throughout your day.

I have often been asked about the difference between prayer, meditation, and hypnosis. To me, prayer is the act of me talking to God. Meditation is me listening. Hypnosis is me talking to myself. I believe they are all part of a continuum. Much like a pendulum swings, I may start with prayer, move to meditation, then to hypnosis, and perhaps back to prayer or meditation.

Paul wrote, "Roger, I just had to tell you that in addition to using self-hypnosis throughout my day, I've been meditating on my greatest expression several times each day. It's the first thing I do in the morning, and then before I make a call to a colleague or client or as I prepare to attend a meeting, I do it again. I am calmer, more relaxed, focused, and I am a better negotiator and boss. Instead of worrying about what can go wrong, I now rehearse easy success."

Supercharge Your Meditation

Many of my clients and I have found that a way to enhance the benefits of meditation is with vagus breathing.

"The vagus nerve represents the main component of the parasympathetic nervous system, which oversees a vast array of crucial bodily functions, including control of mood, immune response, digestion, and heart rate. It establishes one of the connections between the brain and the gastrointestinal tract and sends information about the state of the inner organs to the brain *via* afferent fibers. In this review article, we discuss various functions of the vagus nerve which make it an attractive target in treating psychiatric and gastrointestinal disorders. There is preliminary evidence that vagus nerve stimulation is a promising add-on treatment for treatment-refractory depression, post-traumatic stress disorder, and inflammatory bowel disease."[13]

---

[13] Breit, Sigrid, et al. "Vagus Nerve as Modulator of the Brain–Gut Axis in Psychiatric and Inflammatory Disorders." *Frontiers in Psychiatry*, 13 March, 2018, doi.org/10.3389/fpsyt.2018.00044

In other words, your vagus nerve goes from your neck to your stomach, and it can turn the fight-or-flight response on or off. When you breathe deeply, you stimulate the vagus nerve. This activates the relaxation response, slowing your heart rate and lowering your blood pressure.

Some describe vagus breathing as putting your foot on the brake to stop the stress response. You can do this with a slow breath in through your nose and a long exhalation out your mouth. In doing so, you kick-start the calming "rest and digest" influence of your parasympathetic nervous system. Think of it as getting a dose of a self-made tranquilizer.

When you inhale, information is sent from your lungs to your brain. When you exhale, your brain sends information back through the vagus nerve to slow or speed up your heart. By breathing out slowly, you slow your heart rate, and you relax. When you exhale quickly, your heart rate speeds up, which can leave you feeling anxious. Specifically, it is the slow exhale that activates the relaxation response.

Your vagus nerve is tied to your body's regular daily functions like heart rate, breathing, and processing memories, but it also plays an essential role in the gut. Have you heard about your gut-brain? Your brain and your gut are connected by the vagus nerve. This connection is not only critical to our mental and emotional health but to a host of other health functions, including reducing or eliminating inflammation. Inflammatory diseases such as rheumatoid arthritis, Parkinson's, Crohn's, and Alzheimer's may be influenced by vagus breathing.

Stimulating the vagus nerve can also lead to the inhibition of cytokine production. Overactive cytokine production can lead to the growth of tumors, both benign and malignant, and it may have an impact on heart disease, diabetic neuropathy, cysts, autoimmune disorders, MS, and cluster headaches.

With slow vagus breathing you also create changes in your brain that can sharpen your mental acuity and generate emotional changes that stimulate joy where there was once depression.

Vagus breathing is ancient wisdom. For centuries, contemplative practices of meditation, prayer, spiritual and cultural traditions, movement, chanting, music, and pilgrimages, among others, have taught the importance of slowing the breath.

There are many ways of stimulating your vagus nerve, but you probably know by now that I like to keep things simple, quick, and doable. Here is how I do it:

1. I usually stand or sit but lying down works even better. You can do this with your eyelids open or closed.
2. Place one hand on your navel. When you breathe in, your hand should rise, and when you breathe out, your hand should go back down.
3. Breathe in through your nose to a slow count of three.
4. Hold for a count of three.
5. Breathe out to a slow count of five.
6. Repeat this breath cycle three times.

There are many techniques for vagus breathing. A simple Google or YouTube search will provide you with a variety of methods. Find and use the one that works best for you.

You can stimulate your vagus nerve multiple times throughout your day. You can do it when you are involved in conversations or going for your daily walk. I have found that when I breathe in this manner while riding my bike, my upper body relaxes, and I have more energy.

Let us now put everything you have learned together:

1. Begin your meditation by reading your **Greatest Expression of You** as you breathe in through your nose to the count of three and exhale to the count of five. Continue this vagus breathing throughout this process.

2. Remember Joy. Feel it in your body and memorize the joyful thoughts, emotions, and physical sensations.

3. Mentally Rehearse being your Best Self throughout your day (or next activity).

Sometimes you may find that your **Greatest Expression of You** Meditation may last only a few seconds, and other times you will continue for a few minutes. I find that the two-minute cycle on my electric toothbrush is a perfect opportunity with a modification. I take my three vagus breaths, spend two minutes meditating on being my Best Self while brushing my teeth, and then I take three more vagus breaths.

When you use this process repeatedly with powerful emotion, you can fire and wire new neuropathways and change your life.

In the next chapter, you will learn an easy and effective self-hypnosis practice to keep you on course for being your Best You. So, read on!

Chapter 8

Remind Yourself Who You Are Becoming

"Commit yourself to a daily practice,
Your loyalty to that is like a ring on the door.
Keep knocking and, eventually, the joy that lives inside
Will look out to see who's there..."
—Rumi

How are you doing so far? I hope you are having fun with what you are learning. By now, you are starting to create your future to be greater than your past.

Allow yourself to learn and use the Greatest Expression of You without getting hung up on perfectionism. There is no need to "Do it right." I tell folks to follow along as I teach, practice what they learn, and then make this process their own. This must ultimately work for you, and it should be *your* way, not my way. Remember, the future you are creating is your own . . .

Now, let's take the Greatest Expression of You to a deeper level with mindful self-hypnosis. I view self-hypnosis as a way to remind yourself who you are becoming. It makes no difference if you are using self-hypnosis to close the next sale, to choose vegetables rather than donuts, to improve your relationship, or to reduce pain—these are all about being a better you.

What Is Hypnosis?

Before moving forward, let's take a moment to discuss hypnosis. There is no single, definitive, or official definition of hypnosis. Every definition that you read will be different, and every hypnotherapist you talk to will tell you something different.

For instance, Wikipedia states, "Hypnosis is a human condition involving focused attention . . . reduced peripheral awareness, and an enhanced capacity to respond to suggestion."

The Mayo Clinic defines hypnosis as "A trance-like state in which you have heightened focus and concentration."

Psychology Today calls hypnosis a "mental state of highly focused concentration, diminished peripheral awareness, and heightened suggestibility."

The Society of Psychological Hypnosis, Division 30 of the American Psychological Association, defines hypnosis as: "A state of consciousness involving focused attention and reduced peripheral awareness characterized by an enhanced capacity for response to suggestion."

The International Medical and Dental Association's (IMDHA) definition is, "Hypnosis is an education-communication process that allows a person's conscious and subconscious mind to believe the same message."

The word *hypnosis* does not help us with the definition since it comes from the Greek word "hypnos," meaning sleep—although hypnosis is not sleep.

My colleague, Dr. Richard Nongard, LMFT and President of the International Certification Board of Clinical Hypnotherapy (ICBCH), says that hypnosis really is whatever you believe it is and that everyone makes up their own definition.

I am in alignment with Dr. Nongard. There is no single definition, and I am okay with that. There is an art to hypnotherapy, and we each share our own experiences, methods, and personalities in our expressions of this art.

I tell my clients and teach my students that we are always in trance. I define hypnosis as taking control of the trance that you are in. In other words, hypnosis is the ultimate state of self-control. From my perspective, all hypnosis is self-hypnosis.

Do you remember in Chapter 3 when I suggested that you imagine biting into a lemon? Did you **smell that fresh scent of lemon?** Maybe you had more saliva in your mouth? **Perhaps you even puckered!** I did not force you to imagine biting into a lemon. I told a story, and you chose to play along.

What do I mean by, "We are always in trance?"

Trance occurs naturally throughout your day. It's when you are on autopilot, living your life, thinking about one thing while doing another. Your subconscious mind is like a huge memory bank. Its capacity is unlimited, and it permanently stores everything that ever happens to you. In fact, by the time you reach the age of twenty-one, you've already permanently stored more than one hundred times the contents of the entire *Encyclopedia Britannica*. With all of this stored information, your subconscious mind is capable of handling up to fifty-six different tasks at once.

Remember those times when you got in your car to go to the grocery store and, the next thing you knew, you were parking in the store lot? You do not remember leaving your driveway. You were not even certain you closed the garage door. Somehow you arrived safely at the grocery store, and sure enough, when you got home, you saw that you had closed the garage door.

Or have you ever mindlessly eaten a bag of chips, only knowing for certain that you did so by the empty bag and your own greasy, salt-covered fingers?

What about your worries, anxieties, and fears? What about the negative, self-defeating thoughts that pump adrenaline into your body and put you on full alert?

Do you remember my "Not Good Enough" story from Chapter 1? That, too, was a trance! All of the above are prime examples of how you might enter automatic and natural states of trance.

There exists an unlimited variety of trances:

Stress trances
Anger trances
Depression trances
Self-deprecation trances
Driving trances
Eating trances
Reading trances
Music trances
Sex trances
Talking trances
TV trances
Computer trances
Facebook trances
Exercise trances
Teeth brushing trances

The list goes on and on.

The state of being less than the Greatest Expression of You is trance. This state is what you have memorized. It is your go-to place where you can function on autopilot. As miserable as it may be, it is safe and familiar. The thought of deviating from this comfortable trance puts your body into withdrawal as it works to create the chemicals it has come to crave.

Not all trances run these risks. Enjoyable trances such as being transported to a magical realm with music or books also exist. One of my favorite books is *The Kite Runner* by Khaled Hosseini. He so poetically writes about the farting of the Volkswagen bus in the streets of Oakland that I could hear the pop and feel the vibration of that VW as it sputtered up the street. As I read this book, I could feel pomegranate juice running down my chin when the author described the fruit's tangy taste.

How about you? What are your trances? Think about one of your favorite books and how easily you found yourself having similar responses. Have you ever burst out laughing or started to cry watching a TV show or movie? These are all examples of trance, some pleasurable and some not. This is an example of the willing "suspension of disbelief" for the moment, a term that was coined by Samuel Taylor Coleridge in 1817. When you are emotionally involved in a narrative, you react as if the characters are real, and the events are happening now even though you know it is only a story.

Hypnosis Allows You to Choose a More Helpful Trance

You can learn mindful self-hypnosis to move out of the fear, anxiety, and self-defeating trances and create pleasurable trances that relax, support, and empower you.

Dr. David Spiegel of Stanford University School of Medicine said, "One of the interesting ironies about hypnosis is that old fantasy that it takes away control. It's actually a way of enhancing people's control, of teaching them how to control aspects of their body's function and sensation that they thought they couldn't."[14]

---

[14] Dr. David Spiegel **quoted in** Noonan, David, *Newsweek*, "Altered States" October 3, 2004, https://*www.newsweek.com*/altered-states-129489

When I talk about creating your future to be greater than your past, I am suggesting that you stop the trance of the old story you have repeatedly told yourself. Start mindfully establishing a new story that stems from this moment. Mindful self-hypnosis is about creating a new relationship with yourself. This new relationship starts with recognizing these trances.

My friends and colleagues Kelley T. Woods, Alan Barsky, and Michael Ellner coined the phrase *Mindful Hypnosis* "to describe the engaged, relaxed, yet aware state that empowers a client with the ability to actually *fix himself."*[15] I teach Mindful Hypnosis so that you have the tools to continue creating the changes that you want in your life.

Even with our best efforts, we can slip into old trances and patterns of behaviors. We slip back into unconsciousness. Life is a tapestry of trances, and most of us let everything and everyone else choose the colors and pattern, only to then complain about what we have created.

Willpower vs. Imagination

I think it is important to discuss willpower and imagination. *Merriam-Webster* defines willpower as "The ability to control yourself: strong determination that allows you to do something difficult." It's using your conscious mind to force you to make a habit change. Willpower is a short burst of energy, and it is a lot of work. An example of willpower is telling oneself, "I won't eat those cookies, I won't eat those cookies, I won't eat those cookies," only to then wear down and eat the cookies.

---

[15] Kelley T. Woods and Done E. Gibbons, *Virtual Reality Hypnosis: Adventures in the Multiverse* (2017)

Why does this happen? Because while telling yourself you won't, your imagination runs amok with the senses: feeling the softness of the cookie in your hand, smelling the chocolate, tasting the fat, salt, and sugar.

It has been said that imagination is the most powerful force known to humankind. Imagination, as defined by *Merriam-Webster*, is "The act or power of forming a mental image of something not present to the senses or never before wholly perceived in reality."

This can be both good and bad news—imagining how delicious that cookie will taste can lead to eating too many cookies, while imagining how fantastic having a healthy, slender body will feel can melt away any desire for the cookie.

No matter what, the imagination always wins! Using mindful self-hypnosis, you put your imagination to work for you.

I remember seeing a bumper sticker that read, "Don't believe everything you think." That says it all. We hold our myths—our truths—to be sacred, yet often these truths are fairy tales and horror stories we have invented. We then live according to these fables. We act as if these old stories are happening now, and our bodies respond accordingly. Even when we have experienced real-life trauma in the past, it is only happening now in our imagination.

When you learn to recognize those old thoughts, emotions, and behaviors as imaginations, you discover the power of choice. You realize the power to change these stories and yourself so that when you experience stress, you no longer return to behaviors like binge eating, smoking, or other unhealthy coping mechanisms.

Using self-hypnosis, you are able to exercise control over yourself and your imagination. Hypnosis is a path to a destination. Your focus simply changes from the conscious to the subconscious world. Dominated by reason, the conscious mind deals with rationality and determination. Willpower provides the force to get things done.

However, willpower only goes so far, and making a conscious decision to change is not enough. Dr. Shelley Stockwell-Nicholas describes it this way: "Thought, behavior, and emotion originate in the subconscious mind. If you ask your conscious mind to change a pattern that has its origin in the subconscious mind, it's a little like calling in a plumber to fix your electricity." Or, as my friend and colleague Kelley T. Woods describes it, "Using conscious thought to make change is tantamount to trying to make corporate change by talking to the receptionist. Hypnosis allows you to go right to the CEO!"

Your imaginative world is very real. Its realities have a quality of presence and vividness every bit as insistent as that of the physical objects and beings of the conscious world. In fact, this subconscious, imaginative reality often seems more real than that of the conscious world.

For example, in my twenties, I graduated from college, served as president of corporations, and employed over a hundred people, yet I was still living my life as though I were not capable enough. Regardless of the real world, my inner-world reality was "Not Good Enough."

Using mindful self-hypnosis, you take back your power. The power you gave away to people, stress, food, life, events, and circumstances. The power you gave away to anger, depression, post-traumatic stress, and self-limiting beliefs and decisions.

Your imagination will win, so what are you imagining? Napoleon Hill, author of *Think and Grow Rich*, said, "If you do not see great riches in your imagination, you will never see them in your bank balance."

You might be thinking, "I'm not good at imagining." That is fine. Instead, see, pretend, picture, visualize, hear, feel, or tell yourself a positive story about being your Best Self. And, with a little practice, visualization is a skill that can be developed.

Answer this question: What color is your car?

Now answer this question: How would you feel about driving your car if it were painted hot pink?

Even if you can't create a picture of your pink car in your mind's eye, your reaction, whether resistant or amused, assures you that you can and do imagine.

Light Switch Self-Hypnosis

Enough talking about self-hypnosis—let's learn how to do it.

Begin by creating in your mind's eye your own *Special Place.* (NOTE: I like to think of it as my "Happy Place." Some refer to it as their "Perfect Place" or "Inner Sanctuary." You get to make it your own by choosing what you call it.) Reflect for a moment on your happiest, most relaxing place. This can be a place of contentment, pleasure, curiosity, or peace. For me, this place is outdoors.

- Where are you? (The beach, mountains, forest, a field, or your backyard?)
- Are you walking, lying down, sitting, or standing?
- Is it a warm sunny day? Raining? Snowing?
- What do you see?

- What do you hear?
- What do you smell?
- And where are you now?

See how quickly you got to your Special Place? Accessing your powers of self-hypnosis really can be that easy. You do not always have to go to the same place, but it is usually quicker and easier to go to someplace you have been.

Remember, you are in control of your imagination. If you are at the beach and it starts to rain, bring in blue sky and sunshine if you like.

Most of the time, when I use my Light Switch, I go to Paipu Beach on Maui. I can feel the straw mat under my back. The heat of the sand comes up through the mat. I feel the heat of the sun on my body. I hear the birds in the bushes behind me, the coconut leaves rustling in the breeze, and the waves crashing. I smell the sweet scent of plumeria mixed with the salt air. I am quickly gone and very deeply relaxed. I think it is so cool that I get to go to Maui several times a day, every day!

If you and I are working together, I will always tell you to raise your index finger. Your index finger is the symbol or metaphor for a Light Switch like you would find on a wall. You can leave your hand in your lap, beside you, on the arm of the chair, or wherever is most comfortable for you. Metaphors are the language of the subconscious mind which loves kinesthetic anchors such as the Light Switch. After a few times of consistently activating your Light Switch, your relaxation response becomes automatic.

I don't really care whether you lift your finger, your whole hand, squeeze your fist, tap your toe, or slap yourself; just create a physical anchor to let your body know that it's time to relax—

that you are shutting off the lights, as it were. When you shut off your Light Switch, close your eyelids, relax, and go to your Special Place. When you are ready, turn on your Light Switch and open your eyelids. (It really can be that easy if you let it.) An alternative way of shutting off your Light Switch is to simply look down at your desk, lap, or feet and call to mind your special relaxing place.

When you go to bed at night, do not worry about turning your Light Switch back on. Just shut it off, close your eyelids, and enjoy a night of restful, restorative sleep, waking in the morning relaxed, refreshed, and excited about the new day!

When you are first learning self-hypnosis, I suggest you do so seated or lying in a comfortable place. As you become more experienced, you will discover you can do self-hypnosis in many situations: standing up, walking down the hallway, seated, or standing in the bathroom, riding a bike (eyelids open), playing golf, on the soccer field, taking college entrance exams, or in most any activity. Just do not close your eyelids while driving the car or operating equipment.

For the first week, practice this mindful self-hypnosis technique one minute at a time. For our purposes, a minute is roughly fifty-five to sixty-five seconds. Ask your unconscious mind to let you know when a minute is up. You may want to use the stopwatch on your phone, but I suggest that you not set a timer so that you do not become dependent on the timer. The reason I suggest that you limit it for a minute is so that you learn that you can trust yourself to do this pretty much anywhere and at any time.

As you're rushing between meetings at work and you barely have enough time to stop at the restroom, you have time while you are using the facilities, and you will still get to your meeting on time. After about a week, you will begin to trust yourself to return in a minute's time. You will be surprised at how quickly you can become deeply relaxed. When you have the opportunity, go to your Special Place to relax and breathe. Once you have mastered becoming relaxed for about one minute, then you can go ahead and use your self-hypnosis for longer periods of time. I like to take several three to five-minute breaks (or longer) throughout each day.

Also, this first week, do not worry about giving yourself hypnotic suggestions—just relax. Think about your Special Place. Focus on each breath in and each breath out using the vagus breathing I described in Chapter 7.

I encourage you to use the Light Switch Self-Hypnosis five times or more per day, every day, for the rest of your life. No matter how busy you may be, you can always find five one-minute periods throughout your day.

To help you to make self-hypnosis a habit, I advise that you anchor it to other activities that you are already doing. Some people connect self-hypnosis to opening their eyelids first thing in the morning. I prefer not to do this as it just relaxes me so much, I fall back asleep! You can anchor your self-hypnosis sessions to just before or just after you brush your teeth, to mealtimes, snacks, and bedtime.

Some folks have anchored self-hypnosis to those moments before getting out of the car in the office parking lot in the morning, as well as just after shutting off the engine in the garage when they return home. This method works great Monday through Friday, but then they fall apart on Saturdays, Sundays, and when they are relaxing on the beach in Maui.

What's great about anchoring to routine activities like teeth brushing is that it doesn't matter if you do it at five on Monday morning or nine on Saturday morning. Either way, you get up and brush your teeth, don't you?

Using Reminders

This is the place where people are apt to get into trouble. Either they do not believe me that they need the reminder, or they do not use the reminders long enough.

Think about it for a moment: How old were you when you started brushing your teeth without a reminder? Most children know how to brush their teeth by the age of four, but for most, it isn't until around the ages of eleven to fifteen that teeth brushing becomes their personal rule, not just Mom's and Dad's.

I am not going to follow you around and ask you if you have done your self-hypnosis. That is where the reminders come in. Years ago, when I first learned the Light Switch self-hypnosis technique, I kept sticky notes in my Franklin Planner for two full years before I was finally doing it without a reminder. Please don't expect to make self-hypnosis an ingrained habit in a few days or even a few weeks.

People used to put two sticky notes on one side of the bathroom mirror and three on one side of the computer monitor at work. Today, most people set their reminders as repeat appointments in their phones. Your reminder might say, "Beach," "Breathe," "Happy Place," "Relax," or any phrase that will remind you. You do not have to label your reminder as "Self-Hypnosis" for others to see. I have my reminders set on silent as I don't want dings and vibrations going off when I am with a client. Some people download a free Mindfulness Bell app and set it to go off periodically. You can set it to activate about every hour throughout your day. When you hear that gentle chime, check in with yourself and see what you need, whether that is a Light Switch Minute, a glass of water, or some physical movement.

Practice using your Light Switch self-hypnosis in noisy places. If you can only do it in a soft cushy chair at home with soft music, it is not fully functional. Practice in a Starbucks, the employee lounge at work, the school lunchroom, or wherever you may be. If you are at home, turn on the TV, radio, vacuum cleaner, and get the dog barking.

It is okay to be in a public place like a coffee shop with your eyelids closed. People do not notice. If a friend comes up and starts talking, turn on your Light Switch and start talking. Do not make them wait until you are done. If a co-worker sees you at your desk with your eyelids closed and asks if you are sleeping, say "Yes," or "Just thinking." What you are doing is none of their business. It is normal and natural to close your eyelids throughout the day, so allow yourself to relax.

The Difference Between Relaxation and Hypnosis

Relaxation and hypnosis are two different phenomena. If you are one of my clients or if you listen to my hypnosis recordings, you will likely hear me use phrases such as "deeper and deeper" and "deeper relaxed." From my perspective, the more relaxed you can be during your hypnosis session, the more enjoyable and refreshing it will be for you.

Being deeply relaxed does not make your hypnosis session more effective. It feels better, and it is more enjoyable, but it is not necessarily more effective. Remember, you are always in trance. With hypnosis, you take control of that trance. Negative trances, such as anxiety and binge eating trances, can be powerfully effective at creating what you do not want.

To illustrate progressive states of relaxation, I often use the imagery of a yardstick, where "36" represents wideawake and "1" represents deep, deep relaxation. I suggest that while you are learning the Light Switch self-hypnosis that you make a mental note of where you are on the yardstick with your relaxation. Sometimes you may achieve a "2," while other times, you may only experience a "30." A 30 does not mean you failed or did it wrong. There is no need for judgment. Just notice simply "Isn't that interesting" with no judgment. And when you're freaking out at a 70, getting to a 30 is awesome! It's all relative.

If you have ever worked out with a personal trainer at a gym, you know that they start you out with light weights until you demonstrate form and technique. Once you have mastered form and technique, they start piling on more weight. We are doing the same thing here.

The goal for the first week is practicing form and technique. By this, I mean shut off your Light Switch five times a day for as close to a minute as you can and as deeply relaxed as you can. That is all.

Honestly, if you take five one-minute periods every day for the rest of your life to go to your Special Place and breathe, that in and of itself can be life-changing for you.

But keep reading—there is even more benefit coming up for you. When you have mastered the Light Switch, you can take things to the next level with hypnosis suggestions.

Mindful Hypnosis Auto-Suggestions

To create your future to be greater than your past, you must remind yourself who it is you are becoming. Pairing the Light Switch self-hypnosis technique with hypnotic suggestions is a perfect way to do this.

Hypnosis suggestions, also known as auto-suggestions, are like affirmations, only better. Affirmations are often half-heartedly repeated or listened to with a lack of commitment to the outcome and no real emotional involvement.

Throughout history, people have studied and used the power of the mind to unlock through auto-suggestion. In 1937, Napoleon Hill wrote the book, *Think and Grow Rich,* and completely changed the personal success genre. More than eighty years after its first publication, many people still embrace his lessons. Hill studied self-made millionaires like Andrew Carnegie, Henry Ford, and about five hundred other high achievers in search of a common thread that led to their success. What he discovered was that they all used auto-suggestions and the power of their imagination.

Hill wrote, "Your ability to use the principle of auto-suggestion will depend very largely upon your capacity to concentrate upon a given desire until that desire becomes a burning obsession." Hill said to repeat your auto-suggestion out loud every morning and evening while visualizing it.

Auto-suggestion is a self-hypnosis technique that Dr. Richard Nongard says "dehypnotizes us from the self-talk we tell ourselves and even the words of others we have accepted." [16]

When used effectively, an auto-suggestion, or what I refer to as a hypnosis suggestion, helps you to move out of old, unhealthy trances and create positive, supportive trances.

---

[16] Richard Nongard *The Seven Most Effective Methods of Self-Hypnosis*, p.53, 2019

Tips for Creating Suggestions

1. Keep suggestions short and concise.
2. Use only positive words. Rather than "I'm not stressed," use "I am calm and relaxed."
3. Keep vocabulary simple. A six-year-old child should understand it.
4. Practice using "I" statements, "You" statements, and "He/She" statements and see what works best for you.

For example:

"I feel my body becoming healthier every day."

"You are enjoying eating foods that promote weight release."

"She keeps her promises to herself about healthy eating."

5. Use only present tense words. Instead of "will," "want to," "going to," or "like to," use "I sleep soundly and restfully every night." "I am in the process of becoming the best version of myself."
6. Suggestions should be meaningful and impactful to you. Use action and emotionally impactful words such as "enjoy," "love," or "desire."
7. If your goal is to increase or decrease something, be specific. Rather than "I drink more water," use something like "I drink forty-eight ounces of water or more every day."
8. Hypnotic suggestions are about making changes in yourself, not for changing someone else.

Here Is How to Use Hypnosis Suggestions

1. Begin by writing one, two, or three hypnosis suggestions. There is nothing wrong with only one suggestion at a time—just never more than three. Keep your hypnosis session laser-focused.

2. Passionately read your suggestion(s) five times in succession so that you become emotionally invested. (There is no point in mindlessly repeating your suggestions.)

3. Shut off your Light Switch, go to your Happy Place, and focus on the *outcome* of your suggestions. Do not repeat your suggestions during your hypnosis session, for example, if your hypnosis suggestions are:

   - *I live each moment in joy and hope.*
   - *Joy is in my heart and in my life.*
   - *I choose to be the change I wish to see in the world!*

While in your Special Place, imagine, pretend, see, visualize, or Mentally Rehearse, living your day or life in jubilance and hope and being the change in the world.

If your auto-suggestion is "Every day, I eat food that is healthy and nourishing," run the movie in your mind of only eating healthy food throughout your day.

4. When your hypnosis session feels complete, or when your time limit is up, take in a deep breath through your nose and let it out slowly through your mouth, turning on your Light Switch and gently opening your eyelids.

Although there are advantages to handwriting your auto-suggestions, I also recommend color-coding your suggestions. I have a stack of colored index cards featuring the auto-suggestions I use frequently. My orange index cards are for exercise, the green cards are for running my business, yellow are for academics, blue are personal items, and purple are for relationships.

There are also times when it is not convenient to use written suggestions, such as when running between meetings at work or school. In these instances, go ahead and give yourself hypnotic suggestions using mindful self-hypnosis.

Again, suggestions should be meaningful and impactful to you, so I encourage you to write your own. If you need inspiration for your auto-suggestions, go to my Hypnosis Health Info website and click on *Hypnosis Demystified*. From the drop-down menu, select *SELF-HYPNOSIS,* and from the next drop-down, select *Hypnosis Suggestions.*

Here is the direct link for you:

https://hypnosishealthinfo.com/hypnosismyths/self-hypnosis/hypnosis-suggestions/
You can also find my hypnosis suggestions with images on Pinterest:
https://www.pinterest.com/hypnosishealth/boards/.

Please be sure to take advantage of additional Free Resources for you at the end of this book.

I have more than five thousand Hypnosis Suggestions for you. Feel free to use them word-for-word or use them as ideas to create your own auto-suggestions. When I am looking for ideas and inspiration for new hypnosis suggestions, I search Google for affirmations for the topic I have chosen. For instance, if my topic is exercise motivation, I search for "exercise motivation affirmations." I usually find some great affirmations and others that are not so great. As I read through the list, I often find a word or a phrase that seems interesting, and I write them down. Soon, I will have words and phrases that inspire a new hypnotic suggestion. Again, you are welcome to use my hypnotic suggestions word-for-word, but I encourage you to use them to inspire your own.

I mentioned earlier that you can learn to use mindful self-hypnosis while you are on the go and in a way that supports you. And since you are always in a trance of some kind, why not make it be a more helpful one?

When I am riding my bike up a steep hill, I can think, "This is too hard, I can't do this," or some other negative hypnotic suggestion. Or I can think to myself, "My legs are strong, powerful pistons, I have all the strength, stamina, and energy I need to conquer this hill!" With mindful self-hypnosis, I can choose to suffer as I cycle, or I can choose Joy as I power up that hill.

You may be wondering why I suggest that you use mindful self-hypnosis five times a day and read your hypnotic suggestions five times before shutting off your Light Switch. My reasoning lies within the power of repetition or, as Napoleon Hill described it, persistence.

Author and radio broadcaster Earl Nightingale said, "Whatever we plant in our subconscious mind and nourish with repetition and emotion will one day become a reality."

Importance of Attitude and Language

A positive attitude and a willingness to accept responsibility for your outcome are crucial in ensuring you receive all the wonderful benefits from your self-hypnosis sessions. Your attitude contributes to your success in this program.

If you have an attitude of "I guess I will give this a try," I remind you that in *Star Wars*, Yoda told Luke Skywalker, "Try not. Do. Or do not. There is no try."

Goals that we "try" to achieve usually end up in failure. The attitude behind the word "try" often translates to failure in our subconscious mind. And when you "want" something, you have *wantingness*, but that doesn't mean that you are taking action to make it happen. Other words to avoid are "need," "should," and "must."

The right attitude is one of positive belief and expectation. When you are using hypnotic suggestions for change, a positive attitude of "That is for me. I know that it works!" will propel you to success. By doing so, you get to be empowered rather than a victim of your circumstances. Using the word "choose" as in "I choose to exercise now" is empowering and gives you a sense of control. Another magic word is "yet." "I haven't achieved my goal .... yet!"

I sometimes get the impression that people are waiting for me to wave my magic wand and fix them. (While I do have a Mickey Mouse magic wand, it is only good for laughs.) The magic is within you. When you approach your hypnotic sessions with a positive attitude, you are empowered to garner the results you want in your life.

Use Self-Hypnosis Joyfully!

In Chapter 5, I wrote, "It's not enough to simply state or think about the change you desire once and expect that change to happen. You must affirm your desires repeatedly and with enough emotion (joy) that the new way of being hardwires, overriding old thoughts and emotions that are no longer useful."

One of the many reasons why I love my job is that I learn so much from my clients. A client once asked me if he should bring Joy to mind when using self-hypnosis. I was taken aback by the question. No one had ever asked me that, and I had not previously consciously thought about it. As I sat there pondering the question, I could feel the excitement beginning to radiate through my body. I realized that I do connect to my Joy when I begin self-hypnosis. It is something that has become natural, but I had not previously acknowledged it. The answer to that client's question is a resounding YES!

The benefits of Joyful self-hypnosis seem limitless to me. It is mindful self-hypnosis at its best. One of the added results of self-hypnosis is that it is a way of changing states: from fear to love, sad to happy, and angry to peaceful.

If you want to give your self-hypnosis an added boost, go to that place of Joy that you have memorized and feel the Joy in your body. Next, give yourself your hypnosis suggestions and turn off your Light Switch.

From this place of Joy, you have more energy pulling you to the outcome you desire. This is a much stronger and more powerful way to fire and wire new neuropathways.

Course Correction

I like to think of mindful self-hypnosis as a means of making course corrections. Unless you have a Tesla with autopilot, you drive down the road, continually adjusting the steering wheel so that you stay in your lane. Or imagine you are flying from Seattle to Palm Springs. Once in the air, the plane deviates from its course by a half degree. The pilot, copilot, and autopilot do nothing to make a course correction. One half degree may not seem like much at the time of takeoff but, without a course correction, you will be landing somewhere that is not Palm Springs.

How many times in your life have you set a goal and become sidetracked only to never reach your goal? Mindful self-hypnosis gives you the ability to make the necessary course corrections, remind yourself who it is you are becoming, and make sure that you are being the **Greatest Expression of You**.

Self-Hypnosis Works

I launched My Slender for Life™ weight loss hypnosis program in 1990. Former clients occasionally call to tell me that they want refresher sessions because they have begun to gain weight. The first question I ask is, "Are you using self-hypnosis?" Their answer is always "No," and so that is the first place we start.

All the Slender for Life™ hypnosis weight loss clients who are maintaining their healthy, ideal weight assure me that they faithfully use self-hypnosis. No one has ever said that they are using self-hypnosis and that they are gaining unwanted weight. Additionally, no one has told me that they are maintaining their goal weight and no longer use self-hypnosis. To me, this is a sure demonstration of the power of self-hypnosis.

Most weight loss clients discover quickly that their hypnosis sessions become less about loving peas and carrots and more about being calm and relaxed, having healthy relationships, and living life joyously. With that transformation, healthy eating and releasing excess weight becomes easy. One of the many benefits of self-hypnosis is that you activate your healing and relaxation response which promotes weight loss. Kelley T. Woods, who wrote the foreword to this book, shared with me that "If a client can't come to see me right away, I'll send them your *Orange*

Blossom audio link. When they do come in weeks later, they've already lost some weight!"

The Light Switch Self-hypnosis technique and auto-suggestion method I have described is one way of using mindful self-hypnosis. It is not the only way and may not be the best way for you. If anyone ever tells you that they have the one and only way to change your life, I encourage you to look elsewhere!

My advice is to learn self-hypnosis, as I have explained it. Use it, adapt it, and make it your own. I encourage you to study other methods of self-hypnosis and develop a method that works best for you. I highly recommend Dr. Richard Nongard's book, *The Seven Most Effective Methods of Self-Hypnosis,* as an excellent resource.

You may be wondering if the Greatest Expression of You process is the same thing as mindful self-hypnosis. The Greatest Expression of You is strategic. It is about your Beingness and planning out the fulfillment of being your Best Self. Mindful self-hypnosis is tactical. It is carrying out the plan. I remember a phrase in graduate school that describes the difference between strategic and tactical: "Strategic is doing the right things, tactical is doing things right."

Remind Yourself of Who You Are Becoming

I refer to **hypnosis as a way to fire new neurons** and to remind yourself of who you are becoming. As I have previously discussed, neuroscience teaches us that neurons that fire together wire together. What that means is that if you are having the same old thoughts and emotions and if you are acting the same old way, neurons have hardwired, and that old way of being has become your identity. It is just what you do.

For several years, my wife and I vacationed on Salt Spring Island, B.C., where I marveled at striations ground deep into the rock by glaciers along with the many deer paths that crisscrossed the island. The striations and deer paths resulted, over time, from continuous and persistent glacial grinding and the repetitive travel of thousands of deer. By using mindful self-hypnosis along with the **Greatest Expression of You**, you can create a new path. You have the power to fire and wire new neurons, new thoughts, new emotions, and new behavior. You have the power to change yourself.

At this point, you have all the tools you need to use the power within you to create your future to be greater than your past. Read on and discover how you can maximize the **Greatest Expression of You**.

Chapter 9

Believe and Give Thanks

"Yesterday I was clever, so I wanted to change the world. Today I am wise, so I am changing myself."
— Rumi

Believe

I love learning from my clients. Every day you teach me about life, myself, and new and better ways of creating change. Here is another example:

"You've got to believe it for it to really work," Rita said as we were discussing the **Greatest Expression of You**. Although I had previously overlooked belief as a component of this process, now I realized just how important belief really is. **I knew this** intuitively, and I have implied it, but I had never incorporated the word *believe* into the **Greatest Expression of You**. This insight was a true gift for which I will always be grateful.

It is not enough to repeat the affirmations, memorize the joy, mentally rehearse being your greatest self, and use self-hypnosis to remind yourself of who you are becoming. You need to believe it to achieve it because **we only act on what we personally believe to be true.**

The question is, what is it you believe? Do you believe you can create your future to be greater than your past, or do you believe that you are stuck in your same old story, only to repeat your past?

Your beliefs control your realities. Motivational speaker Brian Tracy said that according to the Law of Belief, **"Whatever you believe with emotion becomes your reality."** You always act in a manner consistent with your innermost beliefs and convictions. According to Tracy, successful people absolutely believe that they can succeed. He calls this positive knowing. Positive thinking, he says, is wishful thinking. Positive knowing—what a powerful mind shift! Just imagine what can happen if you positively know that you can create your future to be greater than your past!

Have you ever noticed you can tell what someone believes by looking at their actions and results? How many times have you set a New Year's resolution to exercise and lose weight? In committing to that resolution, you might go so far as to buy a gym membership or plan healthy meals. But life gets busy. You do not have time to exercise or cook, so you never make it to the gym, and those vegetables you bought go to waste. As the pounds continue to pack on, you decide that you cannot lose weight. Rather than positive knowing, you have a fixed mindset.

You can change that fixed mindset because the Law of Belief is reversible. Remember that neurons that fire together wire together, and you can fire and wire new neuropathways at any age. When you stop firing those old beliefs that no longer serve you, those neurons will separate.

You have probably heard about the placebo effect. Research on the placebo effect reveals amazing discoveries about the power of belief. It also proves that your mind is capable of great feats when it comes to healing your body. My friend and colleague, Michael Ellner, said that your body was created to be healthy, and it was created to heal.

Your body is an infinitely intelligent organism. Long before the invention of modern medicine, we humans have been healing ourselves. Throughout history, healers gave hope, and through expectation and belief, the mind initiated the changes in physiology for the body to heal. The placebo effect is the power of belief.

Your mindset really does matter. A 2007 Harvard study examined the difference between physical exertion and physical exertion plus belief. The researchers recruited eighty-four maids who cleaned rooms in hotels.

They divided the maids into two groups. One group heard a brief presentation explaining that their work qualified as good exercise. The other group did not.

Over the next thirty days, the researchers discovered that the changes in the bodies of the women who had heard the presentation were significant. "The exercise-informed women perceived themselves to be getting markedly more exercise than they had indicated before the presentation. Members of that group lost an average of two pounds, lowered their blood pressure by almost 10 percent, and displayed drops in body-fat percentage, body mass index, and waist-to-hip ratio." [17]

Belief is your acceptance of an idea as being true. You can reinforce your beliefs with Mental Rehearsal and mindful self-hypnosis until they become an automatic part of your thought process. Your belief alters facts and creates the dynamic action that fires and wires new neurons together so that you can create the new you. Simply visualizing yourself having already achieved change, and feeling how that change feels, results in positive knowing.

Athletes who visualize running their event in their mind experience the same muscles firing as if they were running in real life. The brain does not know the difference. (Remember the lemon?) When you believe and visualize that you have already achieved your goal, this is the energy you radiate outward, and that is precisely what you will receive in return.

In your **Mental Rehearsal** of **Being the Greatest Expression of You**, use all your thoughts to produce an elevated emotion so that your body begins to emotionally believe that the future you is already living now. Believe relentlessly in the **Greatest Expression of You**. That is positive knowing!

Along with that relentless belief, give thanks!

"There's a GRATITUDE-CIRCUIT in your brain badly in need of a workout. Strengthening that circuit brings the power to elevate your physical and mental health, boost happiness, improve sleep, and help you feel more connected to other people."[18]

---

[17] Crum, Alia J., and Langer, Ellen J. 2007, "Mind-set matters: Exercise and the placebo effect." *Psychological Science* 18, No. 2:165-171.
[18] Alex Korb, *The Upward Spiral*: Using Neuroscience to Reverse the Course of Depression, One Small Change at a Time. (2015)

A client of mine once said, "Gratitude is the Velcro that holds it all together." We were discussing ***Being the Greatest Expression of You*** and the importance of giving thanks. Previously, I had been describing gratitude as the bow that ties the **Greatest Expression of You** all together, but *Velcro holding it together* is a stronger, more powerful metaphor. To all my clients, I again express my gratitude for being the brilliant teachers you are.

When you give thanks in the morning for being your Best Self throughout the day, your subconscious mind sets you up to spend the day being your Best Self. When you thank your body for having already healed from disease or injury, your body assumes it is true and works to make it so. When you express your gratitude for successfully achieving a goal that you are just beginning, all parts of you come together to accomplish the goal.

What Is It That Makes Gratitude So Powerful?

Think about this: When do you say "Thank you"? After you receive, correct? You are already hardwired to believe you have received the gift for which you express thanks. When you say, "Thank you," your unconscious mind assumes you have already received the gift, compliment, or other gesture someone gives you.

I encourage weight loss clients to give thanks every day for already being at their healthy ideal weight. When you do this, you start eating and acting as if you are slender because your body believes that this future event has already happened or is happening to you in the present moment. In this state of gratitude, you receive.

Neuroscience tells us that the practice of gratitude rewires your brain and creates a cocktail for wellness. When you give thanks, you receive a shot of dopamine. This feels so good that, of course, you want more. You also receive a swig of serotonin, which is the happy molecule. Like an anti-depressant, it enhances your mood, willpower, and motivation. The more you activate these "gratitude" circuits, the stronger these neural pathways become. You also become more likely to recognize and appreciate all that is right in your life instead of habitually looking at what's wrong.

Because neurons that fire together wire together, researchers at the University of Indiana found that the practice of giving thanks builds your brain's ability to spontaneously feel gratitude. Other studies show that a routine gratitude practice creates a healthful and self-perpetuating cycle in your brain. The more you purposefully count your blessings, the easier it is to count them as they happen. Your brain adapts to this mindset. Think of it as your brain having a gratitude muscle that becomes stronger when exercised.

The more you focus on the good in your life, the happier and healthier you are. Studies show that a practice of gratitude improves your heart health, makes you more resilient to trauma, improves your physical and mental health, increases sleep quality, and lowers levels of stress hormones. Toxic emotions are released, physical pain, anxiety, and depression are reduced, confidence increases, and a greater sense of self-worth is realized.

A 1993 study on gratitude and its connection to happiness revealed that voluntary expressions of joy, such as a smile or a few kind words, influence the brain to respond and reflect only positive emotions.

Studies show that the more gratitude one feels, the more their sense of joy increases. Harvard researcher and author Shawn

Achor tells us, "Something as simple as writing down three things you're grateful for every day for twenty-one days in a row significantly increases your level of optimism, and it holds for the next six months. Those who are happy experience 31 percent higher productivity, 37 percent higher sales, 3x greater creativity, and 23 percent fewer fatigue symptoms. Happy people are also up to 10x more engaged, 40 percent more likely to receive a promotion, and 39 percent more likely to live to age ninety-four."

This has been described as a "virtuous upward spiral" in which joy and gratitude mutually reinforce each other. The more gratitude you have, the greater your sense of joy, which results in more gratitude. The more you give thanks, the more blessings you receive to be thankful for.

One way of enhancing the experience of joy is to list the things that you are grateful for. Studies show that just asking yourself the question, "What am I grateful for?" is enough to change your brain chemistry. Before asking yourself that question, take a moment now and notice what you are feeling right now. Do you have a physical ache or pain? Are you feeling sad or stressed? Where in your body do you feel it?

I invite you right now to list five things you have going for you to express your gratitude. (If you are stuck, start by giving thanks for breath.) By giving thanks, you can raise your happiness. By doing this, notice that there is no sadness or stress. Notice that aches, pains, sadness, and stress are reduced or even eliminated. Why? Because when you fire and wire new neurons, you create a new genetic expression. This means that because of that new genetic expression, your immune system is strengthened. Symptoms of disease and illness can disappear and no longer be present.

The Science of Epigenetics

Scientist and author Dr. Bruce Lipton has been at the forefront of the research and education about the science of epigenetics. He teaches that "Epigenetics is the study of cellular and physiological traits, or the external and environmental factors, that turn our genes on and off and, in turn, define how our cells actually read those genes. It works to see the true potential of the human mind and the cells in our body."[19]

Why is this concept important? Because the cells of your body follow the instructions given by your brain through your nervous system, which interprets these instructions. I'm sure you can think of many situations when something said or done caused you to react in a certain way. And, assuming you were with someone, the person you were with may have reacted differently. You may have been angered or hurt by the event while the other person found it humorous.

As your perception changes and you change the meaning of your experience, you change the message that your nervous system communicates to the cells of your body. When you respond with hurt, fear, or anger, the nervous system sends that message to the cells of your body. And when you respond with love and joy, the cells in your body receive a very different message. So, in essence, your mind controls your biology. A person's perception, not genetic programming, is what spurs all action in the body: It's actually our beliefs that select our genes—that select our behavior.

The human body is comprised of fifty to sixty-five trillion cells. Cell functions independent of DNA, and its perceptions of

---

[19] Lipton, Bruce H, "What is Epigenetics?" https://www.brucelipton.com/what-epigenetics/

environmental stimuli affect DNA. This also applies the same principles to the human body as a whole, showing the power our perceptions, our beliefs have over DNA. You literally can change your DNA with your beliefs.

In Chapter 5, I asked you to think of a stressful or upsetting time in your life and then do a body scan for the sensations you experienced and then notice as you recall a happy time, a pleasant time, and how the body feels and how it responds. I like to think of these changes as the Healer's Touch. Now imagine the benefits from experiencing the constant presence of the Healer's Touch.

It's not enough to merely read and comprehend the words in this book. In order for your healing to actually occur, you must integrate these concepts into your everyday life. It's only through constantly interrupting the old unhelpful patterns of behavior, thought, and emotions with self-hypnosis and the **Greatest Expression of You** process that you can achieve self-healing.

Start Your Day with Gratitude

Begin each day, each goal, and each new endeavor by giving thanks. Do not wait until it is over—start with gratitude. Make authentic gratitude a habit. Observe what happens when you spend your day focusing on what you have rather than what you do not have or what's going right instead of what's going wrong. Imagine how you might feel if you focus on the comfort in your body rather than the pain. What message would you be sending to the cells of your body?

When you begin each day by giving thanks for the great day that you are about to experience, and when you start an event by giving thanks for its successful conclusion, you are placing a powerful force in motion.

When you focus on what you are thankful for, you wire your brain to continue finding things to be thankful for. Your brain is created in such a way that you see what you are looking for. Even if you try, you are never impartial; bias always enters your perceptions. This means you do not see things as they are. You see things as *you* are. By regularly reflecting on things that you are grateful for, you construct a filter through which you see the world, and you create more experiences for which to be grateful.

Start noticing people who genuinely feel gratitude. Maybe they give thanks for a flower in bloom, the song of a bird, a hot shower, the giggle of a child, or a loving hug. Watch the shift in them that occurs. Notice how they mindfully open and feel the expansiveness of the emotion. See how they follow it with a kind word or thought. Learn from these people and incorporate their successful behaviors into your life. You know you've unconsciously assimilated their behavioral patterns when you begin to naturally live with gratitude. In Neuro-Linguistic Programming (NLP), this occurrence is referred to as Modeling and is a well-documented method of creating success. You can Mentally Rehearse gratitude and, as part of this rehearsal model, the gratitude behaviors of grateful people.

Another phenomenon of gratitude is that it is contagious. Studies show that when you feel thankful and express it to others, they too, will feel grateful, and express their gratitude to the people in their life. Share the gratitude!

Each day, give a shout-out to someone by thanking or praising them for something positive they have done. Every day go out of your way to be kind to someone. It may be as simple as being purposeful in a smile that you give. Maybe you pay for the cup of coffee for the person standing in line behind you. Make a point each day to do something nice.

In Chapter 10, I will be talking about taking a daily inventory, but you can get a head start right now by writing down at least three good things that happen each day. It is okay if you repeat items from one day to the next.

Now give thanks for the goodness in your life. Laugh loudly. Dance with passion and sing your heart out!

Chapter 10

Daily Inventory

"Self-evaluation directs us to prepare our next performance from the past and today's experiences."
—Oscar Auliq-Ice

Taking a Daily Inventory is an important part of the **Greatest Expression of You** process and a wonderful way to get to know more about yourself. This is a time of self-reflection.

American management consultant, educator, and author Peter Drucker said, "Follow effective action with quiet reflection. From the quiet reflection will come even more effective action."

Drucker understood there is a deep connection between giving time for reflection and being an effective person. The more you know about yourself, the better decisions you will make and the more prepared you will be to live your life.

The **Daily Inventory** is a check in and time for reflection at the end of the day. It is an opportunity to reflect on the ways you succeeded at **Being the Greatest Expression of You** as well as ways you might have tripped up and fell from grace. It is a time to acknowledge your strengths and opportunities for improvement and to recognize in what ways you can act on your potential to make a change in the future.

The two basic components of the Daily Inventory are:

- Review your day and notice the moments when you were your Best Self. Memorize your thoughts, emotions, and actions so that you repeat these successful behaviors in the future. It can be helpful to Mentally Rehearse these Best Self moments to further anchor them in your subconscious mind.
- Again, review your day and notice the moments when you were less than your Best Self and then Mentally Rehearse this same scenario, only this time being your Best Self so that you are creating a new neuropathway to be and do differently in the future.

Hypnosis is often defined as the act of focused awareness. When you Mentally Rehearse, you are acutely focused on what you want to happen. And then, throughout your day, you may wish to further reinforce your rehearsals with additional self-hypnosis suggestions.

There is no one format for taking your Daily Inventory. Almost every one of my clients has their own way of doing it, and as long as they include the basic components, the Daily Inventory is a powerful growth process for them. Personally, I like to make an inventory of myself physically, mentally, emotionally, and spiritually.

I suggest your Daily Inventory be one of the last things you do at the end of your day. I have done it lying in bed, but it is too easy for me to fall asleep. I prefer to do it before I crawl into bed.

When I am at home, I like to go out to my back patio or front porch about thirty minutes before going to bed. I sit in the dark usually with my eyelids open and begin by taking some deep vagus breaths, as described in Chapter 7. I often listen to music and reflect on my day and life in general. When my mind is quiet and I am ready, I take an inventory of my day. For me, this process can vary in time from a couple of minutes to as much as ten minutes. In my mind's eye, I play a movie of the day, and I pay particular attention to these three things:

1. Where did I *be* and *do* well?

I pay particular attention to this so that I can memorize this way of being, as well as the actions I took. I then Mentally Rehearse what I did well, thus establishing neuropathways to repeat them in the future.

As you do this, notice what you were thinking and what you were feeling. How did it feel to be your best self? Play this through your mind's eye and memorize your success.

2. What can I learn from other people's ways of being?

When I notice someone being and doing their best, there may be opportunities for growth for me. I may choose to memorize and Mentally Rehearse these learnings for my own future use.

3. Where was I less than my Best Self? Where did I trip up and fall from grace?

In reflecting on these questions, the goal is not to self-flagellate. Instead, use this as an opportunity to rewind the movie in your mind and replay the same scene again, only this time being your Best Self. By doing so, you prime yourself for success should you encounter this or something similar in your future.

Pay attention and notice **when you fell from grace**—when you were less than your best self. What were you thinking? What were you feeling? Were you being mindful or mindless?

In examining these things, you are laying the neuropathways to *be* and *do* differently in the future. Remember that every experience is an opportunity for learning and growth.

Once I feel complete with my inventory, I give thanks for the day and the blessings I have received. I give thanks for the upcoming night of sound, restful restorative sleep, and for the wonderful day of abundant joy that I will experience tomorrow.

Self-feedback is vital. I do my best to take Inventory following events, looking for how I maintained my Best Self, regardless of the outcome of the experience. I Mentally Rehearse and Memorize how I did that for future similar events.

Even in situations where I didn't do as well as I wanted, taking Inventory provides opportunity to gain meaning and lessons, along with using Mental Rehearsal to imagine myself doing better! When you take the time to review situations where you were less than your best self and then mentally rehearse the same event as being the Greatest Expression of You, **you prime the pump for success.** You create new neuropathways so that, should this same situation occur again in the future, **your mind and body are predisposed for success.**

I received an email from Tom several months after our last session. He wrote:

"Roger, I must thank you for how you helped me when I was going through cancer treatment. I just had my one-year checkup, and I am cancer-free. The work we did help make this possible. But I want you to know that even though we never discussed my career, the Greatest Expression of You procedure that you taught me has helped me to advance in so many ways.

I find the Inventory invaluable. Now, after every meeting that I conduct, I take a personal inventory and explore how I can be better, and then I Mentally Rehearse the improved scenario. My team has gone from lackluster to productive excitement, and my CEO has requested that I co-facilitate a leadership training and team-building meeting.

I'm wondering if I can schedule a session with you to review the Greatest Expression of You process and get your input on how to adapt it and how to explain it to the people who are in the meeting.

Let me know if you are amenable to this.

Thanks."

I happily met with Tom and, the last time I heard from him, his team was fully on board with being their Best Selves. They have especially found value with doing the Mental Rehearsal and Daily Inventory. I love it that they use these individually and as a team.

If you are wondering what you might think about in your inventory, here are some things you may want to consider. Remember to keep it positive!

- Did I embody the Greatest Expression of Me today?
- How did I give care to myself today?
- Did I love well?
- How did I give care to others?
- Who did I help today?
- Did I live my purpose today?

- Was I kind and loving to myself and others?
- Did I treat myself and others with grace?
- What is the best thing that happened to me today?
- What made me laugh today?
- Was I in alignment with my deepest principles and mission? If not, what adjustments need to be made? If yes, how can I make the activity or commitment even more rich in meaning?
- What is my spiritual condition?
- Was I selfish, dishonest, and/or resentful?
- Do I owe anyone an apology?
- Who did I help today?
- How did I make the world a better place today?
- Who had a better day and experience because of me?
- What have I learned about myself and about life today?
- What blessings did I receive today? Have I given thanks?
- What experience did I have today that gives me hope?
- What are some of my reoccurring actions or reactions?

Your Daily Inventory is a way to enhance your self-knowledge so that you can use your energy more efficiently by aligning your habits with your purpose. The more you know about yourself, the more confidence you will have, and the more fulfilling your life will be. When you use your Daily Inventory, you really can create your future to be greater than your past!

Chapter 11

Grace: Loving Yourself Through the Process

"Confront the dark parts of yourself, and work to banish them with illumination and forgiveness. Your willingness to wrestle with your demons will cause your angels to sing."
—August Wilson

You Still Have a Pulse

No matter how much you may meditate on and mentally rehearse being the **Greatest Expression of You**, there will be times when you struggle, when you fall from grace, and when you suffer.

Congratulations! You are human, and you still have a pulse. You cannot walk on water yet. **The Greatest Expression of You** is about being the best human being you can be. It is not about being perfect.

One of the reasons I love the above quote by American playwright, August Wilson, is that to banish our dark side with illumination and forgiveness does not mean the dark side goes away, but that we acknowledge the dark side and move forward.

The Greatest Expression of You is about being your Best Self while living with your shadow side.

I am reminded of the Native American fable about the fight between two wolves. A grandfather and grandson were having a conversation about life.

"A fight is going on inside me," the grandfather said to his grandson. "It is a terrible fight, and it is between two wolves. One is evil—he is anger, envy, sorrow, regret, greed, arrogance, self-pity, guilt, resentment, inferiority, lies, false pride, superiority, and ego."

He continued, "The other is good—he is joy, peace, love, hope, serenity, humility, kindness, benevolence, empathy, generosity, truth, compassion, and faith. The same fight is going on inside you—and inside every other person, too."

The grandson thought about it for a minute and then asked his grandfather, "Which wolf will win?"

The grandfather replied, "The one you feed."

Over the years, I have observed that most of my clients, myself included, have worked to banish the dark parts of ourselves. However, the fight between the two wolves is eternal. Both wolves will always exist inside us. This applies to emotions, behaviors, habits, and every other aspect of our lives. There will be times when we may feel unloving or unmotivated, but we can feed the second wolf by being loving and taking action even when we do not want to.

Too often, we give up in times of struggle. We abandon our dreams and settle for something easier. Somewhere along the way, we got the idea that it was wrong to struggle. We want it to be easy, and it is easier to give in and feed the first wolf.

In his book, *The Heart Aroused*, the poet David Whyte tells us that we don't get to selectively love the part of someone or ourselves that is in the light. We must also embrace the part in the shadow. Yes, you get to embrace your dark side—you get to embrace the first wolf.

David Whyte also wrote an essay, "Shadow," in which he says, "To live with our shadow is to understand how human beings live at a frontier between light and dark and to approach the central difficulty: that there is no possibility of a lighted perfection in this life; that the attempt to create it is often the attempt to be held unaccountable, to be the exception, to be the one who does not have to be present or participate, and therefore does not have to hurt or get hurt."[20]

Being the **Greatest Expression of You** means you live with and embrace your shadow. As a human, you experience anger, hurt, fear, and sadness. These are normal, natural, and healthy emotions. As Whyte describes it, being the **Greatest Expression of You** casts its own shadow.

"Mythologically, having no shadow means being of another world, not being fully human. To live with our shadow is to understand how human beings live at a frontier between light and dark and to approach the central difficulty: that there is no possibility of a lighted perfection in this life; that the attempt to create it is often the attempt to be held unaccountable, to be the exception, to be the one who does not have to be present or participate, and therefore does not have to hurt or get hurt. To cast no shadow on others is to vacate the physical consequences

[20] David Whyte, "Shadow" from *Consolations*: *The Solace, Nourishment and Underlying Meaning of Everyday Words*, Many Rivers Press, 2015

of our appearance in the world. Shadow is a beautiful, inverse confirmation of our incarnation."

Where in Your Life Do You Quit?

There are times when our shadow side seems to surround us in darkness. These are times of struggle. Our thoughts and our emotions of fear, sadness, hurt, and anger come into play. The old familiar feelings and sensations in our body become present, and we want to quit.

Our feelings reflect our past. We've memorized them, and to change is to abandon the past and the familiar. We want the familiar because it is comfortable even when it's miserable.

In Chapter 1, I asked, "Do you believe that it's even possible to be your best self?" As human beings, we all struggle and feel hopeless at times. Sometimes we just want to quit. These thoughts and feelings are normal and natural, and it is okay to experience them. They are part of your story; they are part of your life experience and who you are as a person.

So now that you are in Chapter 11, what have you discovered so far about yourself? Do you believe it's possible to be your best self? Are you creating your future to be greater than your past, or are you still holding on to what is old and familiar? The shifts in your behaviors, thoughts, and emotions can be subtle. Give yourself some time now and notice what has shifted. Have you noticed the many opportunities that you have throughout your life to choose differently? To choose to be your best self?

In my book, ***Becoming Slender for Life***, I told a story about when I climbed Mount Rainier. By 8:00 a.m., we had already been climbing for hours. The summit still loomed massively in front of us. We still had hours to go, and I was exhausted and discouraged. I wondered just whose idea it was for me to do this, anyway. At that moment, the fun was gone. I wanted to sit down and tell my fellow climbers I would be right there when they came down. I wanted to quit.

Then I recognized I was at the point when I always quit. I was having the exact same feelings and thoughts as in other endeavors I felt compelled to give up on. That was the moment when every other time in my life, I had quit. These same thoughts and feelings had held me back in most areas of my life—physically, mentally, emotionally, and spiritually.

So, I stopped thinking about the hours it would take to reach the summit and focused on my next step, and then the next and then the next. Finally, there before me was the crater on the summit. It was a beautiful, warm, sunny day, and I could see forever. By taking one step at a time, I had made it.

I didn't know about the ***Greatest Expression of Me*** at that time, but I did understand that to achieve my goal, I had to think, feel, and act differently than I had in the past.

A few years ago, one of my clients, Vicki, shared with me that she was feeling discouraged because she was tired after walking seventeen miles in one day. At age eighty, she was training for the Susan Komen three-day, sixty-mile Walk for the Cure. I was filled with admiration, respect, and gratitude for her commitment and dedication to this cause.

I must admit, I did chuckle at the fact that she was tired after walking seventeen miles in one day. My response was, "You should be." After walking that far, it is very natural, normal, and okay to be tired. What is important is that she was back walking the next day.

I encouraged Vicki to show herself grace and to remember her own *Greatest Expression of Self* when she felt tired and discouraged. Being her best self, she could acknowledge that she was legitimately tired and also possess the joy and confidence in achieving her goal. Vicki wrote the following for a blog post at Hypnosis Health Info.

It's All about the Journey

by Vicki Browning

"Weighing my ideal weight, feeling fit, and liking who I am are all part of the journey. I enjoy a plant-based diet and attribute my good health to my lifestyle.

My diet is a big part of my lifestyle, and so is my attitude. When people say they can't give up cheese, I just smile. Life is full of choices, and I wonder if cheese is as important as a healthy life, but that might just be me.

I walk six to eight miles and sometimes ten or twelve, and people say they couldn't do that, and I say, "Sure you could if you trained for it." My journey is about staying in condition so I can take a walk when I want to. If I stay in shape and continue to be active, I can continue to travel, go on cruises, and do the things I enjoy because I have the physical ability.

When I was seventy-six, I walked sixty miles to raise awareness about breast cancer and to raise money for research for breast cancer. Now I am eighty and about to do it for the second time. My mother died at age eighty from breast cancer, and I am walking in her memory and raising $8,000 for the Susan G. Komen fundraiser.

My journey includes my choice of friends as well as what I do to keep physically fit. I like to help others, and I like being around others helping others. That's why I enjoyed teaching before I retired and why I enjoy volunteering at the local food bank and why I like to encourage others to reach their goals. That's why I love being a mother and a grandmother and a great-grandmother.

I don't listen to radio or watch a TV show if I wouldn't want them in my living room. I like to read books about people who overcome obstacles. I like reading about the people who made the journey across the country in a covered wagon. The journey was hard, but what an accomplishment. I enjoy watching sports because athletics is about being the best you can be. I enjoy the Special Olympics because the joy of accomplishment is so apparent.

My journey is not complete, but I am enjoying it."

Every time I read that last sentence, I think, wow! What a powerful and fulfilling way to live life. Your journey is not complete, but are you enjoying it?

As I wrote this chapter, I sent Vicki an email to see how she is doing. She is now eighty-four years old and has had open-heart surgery. While her surgeon has told her it will take a year for her to completely heal, she wishes her recovery was quicker. She lives alone, walks to the store, and knows that her purpose in life is to make the world a better place. What a great way to live life being your Best Self!

I encourage you to take a moment right now and check in. Notice where in your life you have disparaged yourself while accomplishing your goal. Did you achieve your goal, or did you allow the first wolf, your shadow side, to hold you back?

Human Emotions

Shame, guilt, and remorse are normal human emotions, and they can be healthy emotions. All human emotions are good.

They are as good as your senses: sight, hearing, smell, taste, and touch. Emotions are like the lights in the dashboard of your car. They are there to give you feedback and guidance.

Unfortunately, sometimes you get stuck in the muck of these emotions, wallow in them, and then compound the situation by judging yourself as wrong. To make matters worse, people will turn to food, alcohol, drugs, or other numbing addictive behaviors to stop feeling their emotions.

Imagine what would happen if, when the oil light came on in your car, you filled the gas tank instead of addressing the oil situation. Again, all emotions are good, and they are for your benefit. Your job is to receive guidance, learn, make necessary course corrections, and get on with your life.

Judgment

In the Bible, Matthew Chapter 7, verses 1–3, we are told, "Judge not, lest ye be judged."

This teaching can apply to our own self-judgment. It is not our job to judge.

When we repeatedly judge ourselves for past actions as wrong, not good enough, or whatever the judgment may be, we are firing and wiring neurons as if the events were occurring at that moment. Ordinarily, the reality is that in the moment of judgment, you are okay. You are going about daily activities, lying in bed, or doing other activities you do.

The event is not actually occurring except in your own mind—in your imagination. Yet your body does not know the difference between events happening in real life and events happening in your imagination. Your body responds either way by producing the same stress chemicals. Over time, these can be harmful to your health.

Self-forgiveness Is Letting Go of Your Judgments

Self-forgiveness does not make something okay that is not okay. It does not create a fairy tale out of past events by rewriting history. Self-forgiveness is not about hoping that time will heal old wounds.

Self-forgiveness involves letting go of judgments of yourself and of others. When you play old memories over and over in your mind and, when you shame and guilt yourself, you return to the moment when the event happened.

As I have previously stated, the problem is that in this moment, that event is not happening except in your own imagination. You experience it throughout your body as if it is happening, but it is not.

The event itself is not the problem. The problem is your judgment of yourself or someone else. When you let go of judgment, you can acknowledge the event for what it was and learn from it.

You can learn how to be and do differently in the future and move on. Letting go of judgment allows you to be the **Greatest Expression of You** in this moment. You are no longer living in the past.

Self-Forgiveness Exercise

The following exercise is one I learned in graduate school at the University of Santa Monica. It is one I have taught to hundreds of clients over the years.

Fill in the blanks:

I forgive myself for judging myself as ____________________.

In the blank line, write the judgment.

Examples: I forgive myself for judging myself as not good enough. I forgive myself for judging myself as unkind. I forgive myself for judging myself as angry.

Next, write a person's name and the judgment you hold of them. I forgive myself for judging ____________________________ as __________________________.

Examples: I forgive myself for judging my spouse as abusive. I forgive myself for judging Bob as hurtful. I forgive myself for judging Mary as controlling.

You see, your actions are your actions. Right or wrong, they occur. Whether these actions occurred one minute or thirty years ago, it is your judgment about the action that eats at you and decimates your self-esteem. It is not up to you to judge. By letting go of judgment, you free yourself from the continued abuse of the action.

Your job is to let go of judgment. Of course, this exercise is much easier when you are **Being the Greatest Expression of You**!

Loving Yourself Through the Process

Times of struggle are opportunities for growth and loving yourself.

Brené Brown, a professor, lecturer, author, and podcast host tells us, *"Owning our story and loving ourselves through that process is the bravest thing that we will ever do."* She explains, "You better be able to tell the truth about who you are and where you come from and what you're up against and like yourself in the process of telling that truth because our sense of worthiness lives inside that story."

She goes on to say that "Wholehearted people learn to own their story and live with authenticity, sense of love and belonging, resilient spirit and a sense of gratitude and joy."[21]

When you learn to own your story, you live with authenticity. As I wrote in Chapter 1, owning your story does not mean repeating it. It means acknowledging it as a part of who you are. Without your past, you would not be you. Now you get to write a new story and create your future to be greater than your past.

The limiting stories you have told yourself in the past may have kept you stuck in old patterns that no longer serve you, but they were what you knew. They were the thoughts, emotions, and behaviors you had memorized. They were the scripts you read from and acted out.

You experienced these thoughts and emotions so many times that they became part of your personality and identity. It is just what you did. You had become addicted to those old stories. But no more.

It can be disheartening to know that trauma affects your brain but remember that healing changes the brain too.

When you love yourself through the process, you understand that it is okay to acknowledge the first wolf. It is okay to walk with your shadow side while celebrating the abundant possibilities you can now create in your future.

---

[21] Brené Brown, *The Gifts of Imperfection: Let Go of Who You Think You're Supposed to Be and Embrace Who You Are*, Hazelden Publishing, 2010.

Grace

As you become more comfortable with being your Best Self, it is time to up the ante. Acknowledge how far you have come and appreciate your achievement. Then dig deeper and allow for more, doing so with joy, grace, and gratitude.

My clients know that I frequently speak about treating yourself with "grace." I suggest that being the **Greatest Expression of You** means you are living in grace. So, what does grace mean?

There are two definitions of grace that stand out for me;

1) "Disposition to or an act or instance of kindness, courtesy, or clemency."

2) "A simple elegance or refinement of movement."

Grace implies a compassionate mindset and caring kindness, and the *Oxford Dictionary* calls it a "Simple elegance or refinement of movement."

I'm sure the scholars at Oxford were referring to elegance and movement of the body, but I encourage you to think of grace as a simple elegance or refinement of movement for your whole being—for the totality of who you are. Imagine living physically, mentally, emotionally, and spiritually in this elegance!

When you are being your Best Self, you treat yourself with grace, kindness, courtesy, and clemency. You display an inner elegance, and you are deliberate in who you are. There is a quiet confidence about you, and you honor yourself with your deeper truth. You acknowledge and illuminate your shadow side with grace.

People tell me that when they live in grace, their mind is sharp, focused, and alert, and yet, their mind is quiet and at peace. They tell me their body is relaxed and energized. They can do more with less effort.

Falling from Grace

Falling from grace happens. You are human. At times, you will forget who it is you are becoming, and you will return to old habits and ways of being. One way to think of the return to old habits is to consider the concept of neurons firing and wiring together.

Those old habits of anger, hurt, fear, sadness, and other ways of being that do not serve you well had become hardwired. They were fused together so that they were what you knew and what you did. Even though you are now firing and wiring new neuropathways, life will happen, and a spark or two will fly between those old pathways.

In grad school, our professors talked about "Stackers." Stackers, they told us, were beings—perhaps gods—who floated around in the clouds, checking to see if they could trip us up. They would hurl a lightning bolt at us to see how we would respond. If we responded with old ways of being, they would laugh and hurl more bolts. If we ignored the Stackers and stayed the course of being our Best Self, they grew bored and gave up. Neurons that no longer fire together, no longer wire together. Or, putting it another way: if you don't use it, you lose it!

Because you still have a pulse you will have times when the Stackers zing a good one at you, and you take the bait. As soon as you become aware you have tripped and fallen, acknowledge it with grace and self-forgiveness. Then get back up and be your Best Self.

Achieve Mastery!

There is a real opportunity for growth during times of struggle. When you love yourself through the process of difficult times, to fall and pick yourself up with grace, **you achieve mastery**. That is real growth.

Being the **Greatest Expression of You** means you learn to walk with your shadow side—your first wolf—while feeding the second wolf. You remember that you still have a pulse, embrace this duality with grace, and love yourself through the process of your life. You cause your angels to sing by shining light on your shadow side!

Chapter 12

My Best Me

"There is one quality which one must possess to win, and that is definiteness of purpose, the knowledge of what one wants, and a burning desire to possess it."
—Napoleon Hill

I live purposefully with a definite chief aim.

By now, I am hoping you have incorporated the Greatest Expression of You into your daily life. You begin each day reading your Greatest Expression, memorizing your Joy, and practicing Gratitude. You Mentally Rehearse being your Best Self throughout the day. Self-hypnosis has become an important part of your day, and it helps keep you focused on being your Best Self. You end each day by taking an Inventory of the day so you can create your future to be greater than your past.

If you have been using these tools, you may have noticed shifts in your thoughts, emotions, and actions. If you haven't consciously noticed these changes yet, I invite you to take a moment right now and consider how you may be thinking, feeling, and behaving differently.

People often report to me that they have begun to live more purposefully. Witnessing this change in my clients is one of the joys I experience in having conversations with people who are actively creating their future to be greater than their past.

As individuals have been implementing these techniques, they commonly dig deeper and explore just what it really means to be "My Best Me." They often seek a clarity of purpose for their life. They uncover a desire be more intentional. They often reflect on knowing their core values and are more focused on what really matters to them. This often leads to me asking, "Why are you on this earth at this time?" or, "What is your purpose in life?" and, "What are your values?"

Core Values

When you know your core values, you know yourself better. Your values are your principles or standards of behavior: your judgment of what is important in life. According to the *Oxford Dictionary*, values are defined as "A person's principles or standards of behavior; one's judgment of what is important in life." Synonyms for values include principles, ethics, moral code, morals, standards, and code of behavior.

We encounter examples of core values in our everyday lives. For example, standing in line at the downtown Seattle Whole Foods during the noon rush amidst hundreds of Amazon employees, I noticed a big sign on the wall that listed the corporation's core values. It read as follows:

"Our Core Values: What's truly important to us as an organization?

The following list of core values reflects what is truly important to us as an organization. These are not values that change from time to time, situation to situation or person to person, but rather they are the underpinning of our company culture."

It then went on with the list of core values.

While I do think our values change over time as we change, have more life experiences, and gain wisdom, I love that Whole Foods states that their values "Are the underpinning of our company culture."

Your values are the underpinning of who you are. To live purposefully and to stay focused on your definite chief aim requires knowing what you value—knowing what is important to you.

Your values determine your priorities. They are the things you believe are important in the way you live and work. Values reflect who you are when no one is watching. If you are being the **Greatest Expression of You**, you are living your values.

Living Purposefully

Knowing your purpose and living with intention gives you the road map for living as your Best Self. Stephen Covey described a purpose or mission statement as your North Star. It keeps you focused, on track, and can serve as a moral compass.

Throughout this book, I have written that you can create your future to be greater than your past. I have discussed how you can write a whole new story—a new script by which to live your life. Your sense of purpose steers how you want your story to go. So, how do you want your story to go?

If you don't already have one, now is the perfect time to create your personal mission statement, one that is comprised of no more than one or two sentences. Make it specific, clear, and aligned with your core values.

Too often, our focus is on success. You can be successful, have a powerful job and great riches, and still be miserable. As theologian Thomas Merton said, *"People may spend their whole lives climbing the ladder of success only to find, once they reach the top, that the ladder is leaning against the wrong wall."*

Over the years, I have known executives at the top of the corporate ladder who are successful, rich, and miserable. Being successful and fulfilling your life's purpose is not the same. I encourage you to pause for a moment and reflect on how you define success.

I have discovered there is a lot of confusion about mission, purpose, and vision statements. Technically, a purpose keeps you focused on why you exist or why you are on this earth at this time. Your purpose is your roadmap for decision-making. Purpose is your definite chief aim.

Your mission statement empowers you. It is a declaration of your purpose and path in life. It is what you do and the core of who you are. Your mission is what you do, whom you serve, and how do you serve them.

Your vision gives you direction. It is aspirational and aligns you with your goal. Your vision communicates your hopes and dreams, which may include what you do for the greater good and who and what you inspire to change. Your vision is the outcome that you want.

While the technical differences have their place, especially in business, we can use the terms "purpose" and "mission" interchangeably. For the purposes of this book, I, too, am using them interchangeably.

Do You Know Your Purpose?

Being a mom or dad is not your purpose in life. Being Mom or Dad can certainly be a major expression of your purpose, but you are here in life to be and do more than that. If being a parent were your purpose, then your purpose would be diminished when your kids leave your nest. Being Grandpa is an expression of my purpose, but that is not my purpose.

If you are living your life without purpose, where are you going? Wandering through life aimlessly is like getting in your car and driving with no destination in mind. Frivolous adventures can be fun on occasion, but given time, you may end up somewhere you would rather not be.

It is not enough to know your purpose—you must live it. Knowing your purpose gives you the ability to aim for the life you want. Living your purpose gives you the ability to choose to do things that truly matter and align with your values and beliefs. When you create a personal purpose statement, you reveal who you are, what you want to do, and why you want to do it.

How often have you said "Yes" to something only to realize you did not want to do it? When you are not living your purpose, you often become bored, and yet, you may be busy with inconsequential pursuits at the same time. In this state, everything feels like work, and you are always tired.

Knowing your purpose in life reveals the true nature of who you are at your core. Knowing who you are helps you reveal your true purpose. This "self-knowingness" makes you aware of when you are living "on purpose" and when you are not.

Take a moment right now and ask yourself:

Who am I?

What is my true nature?

Do I have a definite chief aim?

What is my purpose in life?

In *The Law of Success*, Napoleon Hill wrote:

"It is most appalling to know that 95 percent of the people of the world are drifting aimlessly through life, without the slightest conception of the work for which they are best fitted, and with no conception whatsoever of even the need of such a thing as a definite objective toward which to strive.

There is a psychological as well as an economic reason for the selection of a definite chief aim in life. Let us devote our attention to the psychological side of the question first. It is a well-established principle of psychology that a person's acts are always in harmony with the dominating thoughts of his or her mind.

Any definite chief aim that is deliberately fixed in the mind and held there, with the determination to realize it, finally saturates the entire subconscious mind until it automatically influences the physical action of the body toward the attainment of that purpose.

Your definite chief aim in life should be selected with deliberate care, and after it has been selected, it should be written out and placed where you will see it at least once a day, the psychological effect of which is to impress this purpose upon your subconscious mind so strongly that it accepts that purpose as a pattern or blueprint that will eventually dominate your activities in life and lead you, step by step, toward the attainment of the object back of that purpose."[22]

What Is Your Purpose?

Do you know your purpose? Do you know why you are on this earth at this time? Hundreds of books have been written on this matter, and a Google search will provide guidance on how to find your purpose and create your purpose statement. Keep your eyes peeled for my upcoming sequel to this book—*The Greatest Expression of You Workbook*. If you want to be notified upon its publication, please email me: Roger@HypnosisHealthInfo.com.

Stephen Covey's *7 Habits of Highly Effective People* and *First Things First* are perhaps the most well-known books on the topic of discovering purpose. My favorite is *The Path*, by Laurie Beth Jones.

What I love about *The Path* is that it is easy to read and understand, and the author guides you through a series of exercises. Over the years, I've frequently recommended this book, and the people who have read it appreciated the ease in which they were able to craft a meaningful purpose statement.

I have attended several seminars with Stephen Covey, and I have read his books more than once. I created a Purpose Statement using the Covey format, and I finished with a sixteen-page typed document. Upon completion, I filed it away and, years later, when I cleaned out the file cabinet, I found it, glanced at it, and threw it away. A sixteen-page typed document is not useful for daily living, at least not for me.

---

[22] Napoleon Hill, *The Law of Success in Sixteen Lessons*, Tribeca Books, 1928

Laurie Beth Jones says that a mission statement should be no more than two or three sentences in length, understandable to a seven-year-old, and that you should be able to recite it with a gun pointed to your head. I love that! Using her process, you have a meaningful road map for each moment of your life. Two or three sentences is easy to recall, and it's functional. It is because of Jones's guidance that I suggest your **Greatest Expression of You** be no longer than one to three sentences. Make it useful! My Purpose Statement went from sixteen pages to these five words: "I joyfully empower abundant living." If my thoughts and actions are about joyful abundance, I'm following my North Star.

Focus On What Is Most Important

Once you have determined your purpose, your subconscious mind can direct its thoughts towards your purpose. As I have repeatedly stated, we are always in trance—we are never not in trance, and hypnosis is taking control of the trance that you are in.

According to the National Science Foundation, the average person has about 12,000 to 60,000 thoughts per day. Of those, 80 percent are negative, and 95 percent are repetitive thoughts. Most of these thoughts are directed by the people around you, the media, and your own repetitive thoughts you have learned from your past.

It is easy to drift and let the world fill your mind with fear, self-doubt, and negativity. Remember that when you are remembering past dramas and traumas, they are not happening now in this moment. They happened in the past, but not now. The only place these dramas and traumas are occurring is in your own mind. Your body is producing the same stress chemicals as you play it out now as it did when the drama or trauma happened.

When you live purposefully, and when you are being your greatest expression, you can focus on creating what is most important to you. You can focus on creating what you want versus what you do not want. Using Self-Hypnosis and the **Greatest Expression of You** process, you can now direct your thoughts and emotions and move closer to your destiny.

Embrace Your Shadow Self

Living your values is not about being pious or perfect. It is about being the best you can be while acknowledging your own faults and weaknesses. As I wrote in Chapter 11, we do not get to selectively love the part of our self that is in the light; we must also embrace our shadow self.

When you compassionately embrace your shadow self, you acknowledge the aspects of you that are less than your best self, and you acknowledge where you fall from grace.

In the past, I, too, like many of my clients, have wanted to eliminate those parts of myself I deemed to be *bad*. I labeled these aspects of myself as demons and wanted to cast them out. Today, I have a different perspective. These are parts of me, and without them, I would not be who I am. I have come to realize these parts of myself are tenacious, resilient, and have a strength that I can draw from to be my Best Self. When I am being my Best Self, I can choose traits of strength and make peace with the aspects of myself that do not serve me well in the moment.

When you take an Inventory at the end of each day, you have the opportunity to examine where you fell from grace, where your shadow "self-prevailed," and then mentally rehearse being your Best Self in similar situations in the future.

Stress and Your Shadow Self

Stress management is challenging for anyone with a pulse, and it seems life's stressors bring out our shadow side in full force. Each day we encounter stressors. Some of these stressors are external factors like traffic, work, or family issues. Others are internal. These are the stressors you create in your own imagination. Of course, most of the time, these internal stressors never materialize. You stress over what might happen even though what you imagine likely will not occur.

The fight-or-flight response to stress is natural and automatic. It is what we have known for much of our life, and those old, hardwired programs of fear, anxiety, and anger automatically kick in. This is true for even the most enlightened amongst us. Sometimes people who have been using the **Greatest Expression of You** process for years find that, despite their best efforts, those old neuropathways spark, and the shadow self emerges once again. This is an example of those "Stackers" I talked about in Chapter 11 doing their thing. The good news is that now you can recognize the auto-response and call upon your Best Self.

A Different Response to Stress

A client I will call Jane came into her session excited. She had been learning and implementing my ***Greatest Expression of You*** process into her daily life for four months.

Jane had lost 31 pounds. She started at 190 pounds and weighed in at 159. Her goal is 125 pounds. Stress eating had always been a problem for Jane. Food (especially baked goods like pastries, cookies, and cakes) was the drug that mellowed her.

Work and family stress are high in Jane's life. She has a demanding job at Amazon, and her junior high and high school children are busy with sports, theater, dance, and music.

Jane shared with me the details of a particularly challenging day at work. If something could go wrong that day, it did. She felt stressed and tired, and she started to order a muffin at Starbucks. Jane recognized the tightness in her shoulders and the knot in her stomach. She then used ***Roger's Wiggle*** and asked herself, "Would eating this muffin be my best self?" Jane smiled, focused on the joy in her life, and got on the elevator to her office without the muffin.

The very next day, Jane was caught in traffic getting home from work. This made her late picking up her son and daughter from school, and she had to take her daughter to her dance class. The children were talking loudly and laughing. They were getting along and enjoying each other, but they were loud. The stress of work, traffic, and serving as taxi driver for her kids was getting to her. Jane again felt that tightness in her shoulders and the knot in her stomach. These signals were an alarm going off, warning her she was about to snap at the kids. She asked herself, "Am I being my best self right now?"

Knowing that taking her frustration out on her kids was not her best self, she used the *Wiggle*. She allowed herself to relax and feel joyful. She focused on being the Greatest Expression of herself. She was able to laugh and have fun with her kids.

In both situations, Jane recognized that her shadow self had emerged, and without beating herself up or succumbing to temptation, she let her better self prevail.

Not Just for Lacrosse

I was on the ferry from Bainbridge Island to Seattle when a young man in his twenties exclaimed, "Mr. Moore, the Greatest Expression is not just for lacrosse!"

He looked familiar, and when he said his name, I remembered him. (I will call him Bob.) Bob had been a captain on the Bainbridge Boys' lacrosse team several years before.

I had the privilege and honor of being the sports psychology coach for the Bainbridge Island boys' lacrosse team for eight years. The experience was fun for me then, as well as when I got to connect with some of the guys as they went through college, started careers, got married, and had children of their own.

As we talked during the crossing, Bob shared with me that he never played lacrosse after high school. He shared that he continues to use the self-hypnosis and ***Greatest Expression of You*** techniques I taught the team. Bob said that he used them to get through college, and he uses them now in his career. These techniques have proven valuable in his relationships—especially showing up as his best self with his fiancée.

To my delight, Bob talked with me about how recognizing his shadow self has made him a better man and partner. He thanked me profusely for introducing him to his shadow self. He said that having a name for that part of himself gave him the power to be and do different and to be his Best Self.

Intention for the Day

Bob still has his Greatest Expression posted on his bathroom mirror and uses it to create his intention for the day every morning. At first, his fiancée did not know what to think, but he explained it to her, and she loved the results. She especially loved that he was so purposeful in his intention to be his Best Self for the day. She has now posted her statement next to his on their bathroom mirror.

Bob grinned when he said that his fiancée was really good at gently reminding him when he wasn't being his best self! We laughed and agreed that we need people in our lives who love us enough to help pull us up along the way.

Bob uses the stress reduction techniques I taught the team, and he and his fiancée both listen to ***Orange Blossom*** from time to time.

He went on to say that he and his fiancée use Mental Rehearsal to create a positive fantasy of their future together. Bob said that they discuss their goals and dreams and write them down. Each of them has a copy. Together they do a Master Mind, and then they individually Mentally Rehearse making it happen.

Over the years, there were moments when I looked at the team of teenage guys and wondered if anyone was listening. They were! Hearing stories like this from former lacrosse team members was one of the many wonderful rewards that I received for volunteering with these guys, and this gives me hope for the future.

Speaking of hope, the next chapter is all about hope. When you live your **Greatest Expression of You**, *Hope is Realistic!* (As my friends Kelley T. Woods and Michael Ellner would say.)

Chapter 13

Hope

"Hope is the thing with feathers that perches in the soul and sings the tune without the words and never stops at all."
—Emily Dickinson

I like the sound of the word "hope." Just thinking about hope tickles my soul and warms my heart. When I think about hope, I am reminded of the old hymn, "Whispering Hope."

"Soft as the voice of an angel
Breathing a lesson unheard
Hope with a gentle persuasion
Whispers her comforting word

Wait 'til the darkness is over
Wait 'til the tempest is done
Hope for the sunshine tomorrow
After the darkness is gone"[23]

---

[23] Septimus Winner, "Whispering Hope" (1868) Timeless Truths library https://library.timelesstruths.org/music/Whispering_Hope/

Hope is always present, and it is the hope that tomorrow will be better than today—that we can create our future to be greater than our past—which gave birth to the **Greatest Expression of You**.

My mom was one of the most hopeful people that I have ever known. For her, hope wasn't a feeling—it was a state of being. Even in the months and weeks prior to her death, she talked about her family, her travels, and the places she wished she could have visited. Even though she knew she would never get to visit New York City, she expressed neither bitterness nor hopelessness. Just thinking about what it would be like to see the Rockettes dance live on stage gave her joy. And when her ninety-six-year-old knees hurt, she would say, "This too shall pass." My mom didn't focus on the problem—she focused on what she desired.

Hope and optimism are important to our physical, mental, emotional, and spiritual well-being. Hope and optimism are frequently used interchangeably. Volumes have been written about their similarities and differences. Most scholars view hope as an emotional experience and optimism as an intellectual practice.

In one study, the authors concluded, "Hope is distinct from optimism by being an emotion, representing more important but less likely outcomes, and by affording less personal control . . . When people do have a high degree of control, they may no longer need to be just hopeful but can be optimistic because the outcome is now attainable."[24]

---

[24] *Bruininks, P., Malle, B.F. "Distinguishing Hope from Optimism and Related Affective States," "Motiv Emot" 29, 324–352 (2005).* https://doi.org/10.1007/s11031-006-9010-4

An article in the *Journal of Positive Psychology* suggests that hope and optimism are not that strongly related to each other. Personality psychologists Gene Alarcon, Nathan Bowling, and Steven Khazon state: "Simply put, the optimistic person believes that somehow—either through luck, the actions of others, or one's own actions—that his or her future will be successful and fulfilling. The hopeful person, on the other hand, believes specifically in his or her own capability for securing a successful and fulfilling future."[25]

In a 2014 Commencement Address, Bill Gates said: "Optimism for me isn't a passive expectation that things will get better; it's a conviction that we can make things better—that whatever suffering we see, no matter how bad it is, we can help people if we don't lose hope and we don't look away."[26]

I view optimism as a choice to think and act positively. It is the choice to see the glass as half full and to know you can fill it so that it overflows. Optimism is hope in action. When you persistently use hope and optimism together, you can create your future to be greater than your past.

Author Anne Lamott wrote, "Hope begins in the dark, the stubborn hope that if you just show up and try to do the right

---

[25] Gene Alarcon, et al "Great Expectations: A Meta-Analytic Examination of Optimism and Hope" *The Journal of Positive Psychology* **quoted in** Dholakia, Utpal, Ph.D. (February 26, 2017) "What's the Difference Between Optimism and Hope?" *Psychology Today* https://www.psychologytoday.com/us/blog/the-science-behind-behavior/201702/whats-the-difference-between-optimism-and-hope

[26] *Stanford News*, Stanford Report (June 15, 2014) Text of the 2014 Commencement address by Bill and Melinda Gates https://news.stanford.edu/news/2014/june/gates-commencement-remarks-061514.html

thing, the dawn will come. You wait and watch and work: you don't give up."

Hoping for the best is not enough to get better. It doesn't necessarily result in getting better either. Hoping for the best is focusing on something you would like to happen, which may or may not occur.

Hope is not abandonment of personal responsibility. For some people, the term hope implies a line of thinking such as, "I want this to happen, but it is not necessarily tied to my actions or my reality. I want it, but I don't want to do what's necessary to achieve it, so I'll just hope for it."

This can be described as wishful thinking, magical thinking, or even delusional thinking. It can help us feel good, but the fact that we feel good does not necessarily mean things are okay. Unrealistic hope is a passive wish which may cause despair. It may be fantasy, and it carries negative feelings.

Realistic hope is based on achievable, realistic expectations. Realistic hope is an active, analytical process. It involves an assessment of the future, perseverance, and expectancy. Realistic hope requires an appraisal of all the possibilities and their consequences, promoting the realization of the hope and its expectancy. It is an important ingredient of living and of a fulfilled life.

There is no such thing as false hope. In practice, false hope refers to when a person speaks as though they are hopeful but doesn't really believe in the power of hope. They actually feel hopeless. Their unrecognized inner conflict can produce the reverse effect.

Clear-eyed hope gives us the courage to confront our circumstances and the capacity to surmount them. For all our patients, true hope has proved to be as important as any medication.

Neuroscience has taught us that hope, belief, and expectation can block pain by releasing endorphin and enkephalins (natural opiates) in a process similar to the effects of morphine. When the emotions of hope and the conscious thoughts of optimism are working together, healing can occur. Hope can also have important effects on physiological processes like breath, blood flow, and motor function.

When firing and wiring new neuropathways, it is hope combined with joy that acts as the glue connecting new pathways together.

Hope is the emotion at the heart of the **Greatest Expression of You**, and it is at the heart of healing. Hope is an act of defiance when things seem hopeless.

While working at a cancer center, I once took an emergency call to meet with a man who had just been told his prognosis was bleak. The treatment regimen available for his cancer was brutal, and the odds that the treatment would work were less than favorable.

When I walked into the room to meet him for the first time, he was looking at a picture of a young girl. We introduced ourselves, and I sat down next to him as he told me his story. He expressed his hopelessness and saw no point in participating in the recommended treatment. Even with treatment, the odds were that he had weeks, maybe a few months, to live.

He also told me about the physical pain he was experiencing. His heart had stopped several times because of his previous cancer treatment. In the process of resuscitation, his ribs had been broken. Any movement was painful, and lying flat was excruciating. For him to receive radiation, he would have to lie still on a table for markings for each treatment. He did not think it would be possible for him to get onto the table and lie down with his broken ribs. He was ready to go home and die.

As I listened to the depths of his despair, I asked about the picture he was looking at when I entered the room. He shared with me that the photo was of his four-year-old granddaughter. I told him that I had five granddaughters. His eyes lit up as he asked me about them. As we exchanged our grandfather stories, I asked him what he hoped for his granddaughter. He came to life and opened his grandfatherly heart. He hoped she would be healthy, happy, and excel in school. He had hope that she would go off to college and have a successful career, marry the love of her life, and have a wonderful family of her own. In her, he had hope.

He decided to see if he could lie down for the marking. I used hypnosis with him, and then we walked into the room for marking. I continued talking with him as he lay down on the table. I helped him control his breathing. While the marking occurred, I stood in the booth and guided him hypnotically on the mic as he successfully completed this segment of the procedure.

We met again the next day as he began his treatment before, during, and after radiation. We talked about the **Greatest Expression of You** and about living with Hope and Joy—even if he was dying from cancer.

We met several more times, and he began to respond to the treatment. Now, several years later, he is alive and in complete remission from cancer. The hope that he had for his granddaughter sparked a seed of optimism for a bright future for her. That hope was the motivation he needed to go for the treatment.

It was several months after treatment concluded when he said to me that he did not know if he would live to attend his granddaughter's wedding but that he was excited to be there for her first day of kindergarten! For several years now, he has wished me a Merry Christmas and updated me on his active life. He continues to eagerly tell me about his grandchildren. He now hopes one day to tell me about his granddaughter's wedding!

Over many years I have met with people who were very discouraged and ready to give up. They were filled with despair and doubt, and they were ready to throw in the towel and quit.

I have also met with people who are successful in most areas of their life. They have family, jobs, money, and big houses. Yet, they are dissatisfied. I often hear laments of a lack of purpose. It is as if they have walked on the moon, and now there is nowhere else to go. They are stuck as life passes them by.

The most content, happy, and successful people I coach are still going strong. Often these clients are retired, but they continue to work at bettering themselves and contributing to the world around them. One thing that sets these people apart is that they have hope. They are doing what they do today to create a better tomorrow.

A common trait I have noticed in people who live in hope is that they find ways to improve themselves. They do not wait until they are "sick" to do so. Have you ever considered that you do not have to be sick to get better? People who live with hope do not wait to be sick to get better.

Sometimes clients schedule a "mental massage" with me. I have met with one woman in particular about once every three or four months for several years now. When I first met Janet, she came to me for weight loss. She lost almost sixty pounds with my Slender For Life™ weight loss hypnosis program, and she has kept it off. Since then, she has chosen to schedule quarterly appointments because she loves her mental massage. Janet considers this experience one of the nurturing self-care gifts she gives to herself. Her sessions with me are as important to her as her mani-pedis and massage therapy.

One of the attributes I love about Janet is that she is always seeking new opportunities for growth and healing. She works out in the gym to be physically stronger. She seeks out new adventures to challenge her body in different ways. It isn't that she is dissatisfied with who she is. Not at all. Janet esteems herself highly.

But she has come to understand that with every thought and feeling, she is performing epigenetic engineering on her cells. Janet understands that by changing her mind, she is changing her body. And that by changing her body, she is changing her mind. She is filled with hope for herself, her family, her friends, her country, and the world around her. Janet believes and works for a better tomorrow.

If you were to know Janet, you would know that she is healthy and happy. She is living abundantly. She is satisfied with who she is. But that doesn't keep her from getting better. Janet lives in hope and is not willing to sit back on her laurels and coast.

Janet loves the **Greatest Expression of You** process because she knows that with every thought and feeling, she can build a neural network focused on the broadcasting of positive healing and joyful impulses. As happy and satisfied as she is today, she lives for a better tomorrow.

How about you? Just how much greater can your future be? How much better can you be? How much more hope, joy, and happiness can you have?

Are You at Your Upper Limit?

I have witnessed people create loving relationships, secure their dream job, or achieve a monumental life goal and finally feel as though they have attained genuine happiness only to become overwhelmed with stress, anxiety, doubt, fear, and depression. I have also heard from others that the thought of creating positive changes in their life means that they are not currently okay or that they are less than someone else. To protect their self-image, they resist change. They resist exceeding the success they have achieved thus far in life. Some people have shared with me that creating more joy and abundance in their life would seem selfish, and they are reluctant to hope for more.

These are three examples of people who are at their upper limit. Author Gay Hendricks first coined the term "Upper Limit" in his book, *The Big Leap*. Your Upper Limit is your tolerance cap for how much more hope, joy, happiness, and abundance you will allow yourself.

To create your future to be greater than your past does mean getting out of your comfort zone. Unfortunately, too often, we trade being our best for comfort. (Remember, neurons that fire together wire together, and those old comfort neurons are very addictive.) Even when we do achieve something extraordinary, we are not able to process the wonderment and gratitude we feel if we are not used to feeling that much happiness and joy. We literally go into withdrawal for comfort, leading us to self-sabotage and ensuring we stay within our safe zone.

Who would have thought that too much hope, joy, and happiness would be foreign and potentially dangerous? There is one more potential pitfall: When we have everything we want, we are more vulnerable than ever before because we could lose it all. So instead of joyfully living in gratitude, we may become more paranoid and neurotic because we have more to lose.

Can you conceive your life being better, being happier, having more love, more hope, and more abundance?

As I see it, if you have a pulse, you still have room for growth. You still have opportunities for learning. There are still issues for you to work with, and you can still become a better version of yourself. No matter how wonderful your present may be, your future can be even greater.

Opportunities for Learning

So, what opportunities for learning will you take advantage of? There are so many possibilities for getting better that the list is endless. Here are some ways to help you stimulate your own thinking:

- Learn hypnosis
- Meditate
- Explore and enhance your spirituality
- Go to school or complete your degree
- Become a Master Gardener (to me, planting a seed is a sure sign of hope!)
- Learn to paint
- Take music lessons
- Travel
- Ride a bike

- Go hiking
- Learn to swim
- Be a volunteer
- Regularly visit a senior citizen
- Help at a special needs preschool
- Try hypnotherapy, chiropractic, acupuncture, biofeedback, craniosacral therapy, massage, qigong, Reiki, and/or the many other healing therapies available

I invite you to take a moment right now and start a list of ways you can create your future to be greater than your past. The possibilities are endless. As long as you have a pulse, keep getting better.

Love and Give

I remember a conversation about life with my grandmother. She was in her nineties and still living alone in her old, drafty Iowa farmhouse on her meager social security. She got up every morning, ate, read the Bible, and prayed. She read the paper, listened to the radio, and she went to bed.

Grandma and I were talking about purpose, career, goals, and living life. I asked her what got her out of bed in the morning, and she did not hesitate to answer. "To pray for you and all my children and grandchildren, to read my Bible, and water my plants."

My grandma was clear about her contribution and about continuing to better herself. She was happy and content. She loved, and she gave. Grandma had so many stories to tell about growing up in the 1890s, learning English at age eight, and raising seven children.

She did not seem to ever want for more, but she was an avid reader and kept up on the daily crossword puzzle. She loved to discuss what she was reading and hearing on the radio. Even though she continued to learn, hope, joy, and love were all that she needed.

Make Lemonade

I have noticed that the people who are the most successful at using the **Greater Expression of You** process and achieve the best results are the ones who are already happy and have purpose in their life. It is important to note that these same people are my clients because they are dealing with challenges.

Disease, pain, and life's trials and tribulations are part of our human experience. They are my clients because they want to better themselves, and they want to keep on going. They keep on becoming their Best Self. No matter what, they love, and they give. They don't stop just because life handed them a lemon. **The Greatest Expression of You** is not a destination. It is a journey, so keep going. Love and give.

Planting Hope

A metaphor I love to use with clients goes something like this:

"I know folks who talk about planting seeds...even to the point of growing their own food...just to be able to independently nourish the self...you know how it works...you just dig the hole in the ground...sprinkle in some seeds...there's nothing more to see just yet...but there's a feeling...a very strong positive feeling... that there's something important about to happen...and it may seem to take a while...but you can anticipate with enthusiasm...that the seeds you planted will surely yield something quite valuable..."

My hope for you is that you do create your future to be greater than your past. I have some favorite quotes about hope that I am choosing to use to close this chapter.

- "Hope is a powerful thing. It inspires us to do the impossible and helps us carry on during difficult times. And hope can come in many different shapes and forms. It may be through our favorite music, or a good book, or even by listening to our favorite thought leaders." —author unknown
- "You may not always have a comfortable life, and you will not always be able to solve all of the world's problems at once but don't ever underestimate the importance you can have because history has shown us that courage can be contagious, and hope can take on a life of its own." —Michelle Obama
- "Hope is important because it can make the present moment less difficult to bear. If we believe that tomorrow will be better, we can bear a hardship today." —Thich Nhat Hanh
- "Hope is being able to see that there is light despite all of the darkness." —Desmond Tutu
- "Hope is a waking dream." —Aristotle

It is with hope and joy that I expect great things to happen as you create your future to be greater than your past!

Chapter 14

Creating Your Future to Be Greater than Your Past

I am excited by the person I see myself becoming.

Putting it All Together

At the end of his last session, an online client said, "You have the plan all laid out. It's up to me to follow it." Those words were so joyous, I did a happy dance in my desk chair. He is ready to move forward in his life without my assistance.

The plan he was referring to is my **Greatest Expression of You**. So how about you? Are you following the plan? Are you reading your **Greatest Expression of You** every morning? Are you meditating on it, memorizing the joy, and mentally rehearsing being your greatest self?

Do you use your self-hypnosis throughout the day to remind yourself who you are becoming? Do you take an inventory at the end of your day? Do you notice where you did well? Do you mentally rehearse what worked? Do you notice where you did not do so well and then mentally rehearse being and doing differently in the same situation next time?

When you live as if you are being your Best Self, your body does not know whether you've imagined it or *are* it. Either way, your body produces the same chemicals and moves you in the direction of being your Best Self. Additionally, the areas of your brain that generate positive thoughts and emotions physically increase.

I encourage you to hold the belief that you are becoming the **Greatest Expression of Yourself** and to give thanks for this blessing. Remember, your body knows that when you say, "Thank you," you have already received. Living in gratitude opens you up to receive.

So, now what? You may be wondering, "What is the point of all of this, anyway?!" Do not just take my word. Here is what Julia wrote to me in an email:

"I contacted you because I wanted to lose weight. But I had no idea how much my life would change. Yes, I've released over fifty pounds, and I have fifteen more to go. I have no doubt that I will achieve this goal, but for the first time in my life, I know I won't put it back on. In all honesty, now the weight loss seems incidental. What I've learned from you and how I've been able to change my life is far more important to me now. Even if I hadn't lost a pound, this journey has far exceeded my expectations."

As I read this email, I felt honored to have had the opportunity to be her guide in this part of her journey. I overflowed with joy and excitement for her. I wrote back and thanked Julia for sharing. I then asked how specifically her life had changed.

Here is her reply:

"As a professional, I have known that I am good at what I do. I'm highly respected, looked up to, and am often asked to be in leadership positions. And yet, I felt isolated and alone. I had no friends. No one in the office ever came to say "Hi" or asked to go out to lunch with me or invited me to go with the staff for happy hour. It had been almost thirty years since I was even on a date.

Food, especially anything baked, and chocolate became my constant companion. I always knew where I could find a chocolate chip cookie. Chocolate was always there for me and never let me down.

Honestly, I thought your request for me to write two or three sentences about being my Best Self and reading it every morning was silly. Being the compliant perfectionist that I am, I did it anyway.

My greatest expression of me is '*I am open, warm, friendly, and loving. I listen with compassion and let others know that I care.*'

I began to notice that people smiled at me when I walked into the office, and I smiled back. I started saying 'Good morning,' and they would say it back to me, and some even asked, 'How are you?' Rather than sitting by myself in the employee break room, I sat down with others and asked about them. People began to come and sit with me, and soon I was going out to lunch with them, and three nights in a row, we went to happy hour. (Don't worry, I've since moderated that.)

My first thought was, 'Why have they changed, and why do they want to be with me?' And then I realized how much I had changed. I used to have my wall up so high that no one could get over it. They didn't change, I did....by being my best me.

And guess what? A man has asked me out on a second date!"

I immediately received a follow-up email from Julia:

"P.S. I frequently sit in the break room now near or next to the chocolate, cookies, and doughnuts, and they absolutely have no appeal. I often don't even notice that they are there unless I see someone else as they reach for one."

My wish for you is that Julia's experience gives you hope for what may be possible for positive changes in your life.

So, who is it that you are becoming? If you are being your Best Self, what is your life like? I invite you to take some time right now and reflect on these questions. You can even challenge yourself and journal your response.

Or are you holding back from making changes in your life that allow you to create your future to be greater than your past? Do you need to hold yourself back? What if you did not hold yourself back?

A lot of things can stand in the way of being your Best Self. Making changes can be challenging even for the most enlightened and self-actualized among us.

Perhaps you have thoughts and fears that could be hindering your desire to move forward in your life. Not only are you having to manage your own thoughts and emotions spurred by the changes you are making, but you may also experience unsupportive reactions from family and friends. You may be asking why the people you are closest to wouldn't support you in bettering yourself.

We create our own gestalt or perceptions of the people in our life. The scenario goes something like this: Judy and Donna have been best friends forever and meet up at a local café for coffee and pastries several mornings each week. Both women are significantly overweight, but eating those doughnuts, long johns, and cinnamon rolls brought them together in ritual.

Without telling Judy, Donna met with me for a weight loss consultation and signed up for my Slender for Life™ weight loss hypnosis program. After her first session, Donna stopped eating pastries and ordered oatmeal instead. She still wanted to have coffee with Judy, and it did not bother Donna that Judy had her pastry. By the end of the second week, Judy began to cajole, plead, and even tried to guilt Donna into succumbing to a pastry.

Donna had shared with Judy that she was doing hypnosis for weight loss and told her she no longer desired pastries. Judy feigned support but continued to offer Donna "Just one bite." Judy became distant and less talkative as the weeks went on. Donna was losing weight as Judy continued to gain weight.

By the end of the second month, Judy started frequently canceling their coffee dates and sometimes simply stood Donna up. When Donna tried to talk to Judy about what was going on, she became very emotional and said she felt abandoned by Donna. It took them almost a year to work through the emotional upheaval. A few months later, Judy called for a consultation and began to lose weight with weight loss hypnosis. The last time I talked with them, they were going for long morning walks, stopping for coffee and oatmeal.

I have heard many similar stories over the years from people trying to create change in their life. Loving spouses, partners, siblings, parents, children, friends, and colleagues can easily feel threatened. You may think you are the one making the change, but your change affects other people in your life too. They have their understanding of who you are, and your change messes with their reality. How dare you do that! This is a totally normal human experience. When people you love and who love you are struggling with your change, remember to Mentally Rehearse being with them as your Best Self and respond with love.

I encourage you to acknowledge upfront that there will likely be obstacles along this journey toward creating your future to be greater than your past. When you discover something that is standing in your way of achieving your goals, you have choice. You can choose to give up and avoid the challenge, or you can find a way over, under, around, or through the obstacle.

The difference between giving up or moving forward is the decision you make. You create your future to be greater than your past by making the commitment to yourself and then taking that first step into the unknown.

An obstacle that many of us create is fear of failure. We may doubt ourselves: "What if I can't do this?" "I've never been successful before, so there's no point in trying."

If these thoughts come up, ask yourself this: "What does failure even mean?" Does it mean we are not making progress? Heavens no! Change does not occur in a straight line—it is more like a spiral. When you fall from grace, get back up, look how far you have come, and then take the next step forward. The only failure is to not do it at all.

Managing Your Expectations

In Chapter 11, I shared Vicki Browning's story, *It's All about the Journey*. With her permission, I share her story as a blog post and in this book. Her story has generated stimulating conversations about managing expectations.

The Greatest Expression of You process is not about magical thinking. It is all about your attitude—your *beingness*. Being your Best Self, you are managing your expectations.

When you mentally rehearse your day or a specific event, you are rehearsing how you will show up and *be* in this world. You are not planning a chain of events exactly as you want them to happen or dictating to the universe winning lottery numbers—that is magical thinking.

Magical thinking is planning an event exactly as it will go and expecting it to turn out exactly as you had wanted. Do not get me wrong. There is certainly value in mentally rehearsing the details of an event as you want them. It can help you through the event or even improve your golf swing.

But, if you really want to make God laugh, tell Him your plans! Just because you mentally rehearsed winning the lottery does not mean that you will—especially if you do not buy a ticket.

You can, however, mentally rehearse the details of an event with an attitude of gratitude, and you can allow for things to be different and even better. Sometimes when you plan for a new white Ford, you get a slightly used red Mercedes. What you received was different than your plan, but it was bigger and better!

When you mentally rehearse your day or an event, you are laying a plan with your goal in mind. Throughout your day, as you act on this plan, there are twists and turns. It is not your job to force or control the course. Your job is to create the plan and then to make course adjustments that lead you to your goal. If you are inflexible and refuse to go with the flow, if you refuse to make course adjustments, you end up stuck in the ditch.

As you live your day, be aware of those old thoughts, emotions, behaviors, and physical sensations that no longer serve you. Again, remember that you are still human and have a pulse. The goal is not to never experience those old thoughts and emotions again; the goal is to empower yourself to change them to thoughts and emotions that serve you.

When you recognize the fear, hurt, anger, or sadness, check in and ask yourself, "Am I being my Best Self?" If the answer is "No," then recall your *Greatest Expression* and memorize the joy. At that point, you can respond as your Best Self.

Your private thoughts and self-talk really do matter. Isn't it time to fill your mind with loving, healthy, positive, and prosperous thoughts?

Here are some emails that I have received from people who are using **The Greatest Expression of You**.

My Life Changed

"Roger, my life changed thanks to your Greatest Expression of You," wrote another young man who just graduated from college.

I met you when I was a senior and played on the Bainbridge Boys Lacrosse team. I met with you privately several times, and you taught me the *Greatest Expression of You*.

I went from being careless, lazy, and angry and skating through school to where I am today. I just graduated with honors as a premed student. I am in a committed relationship. I am happy and excited about med school.

I taught my partner your Greatest Expression of You process. We read your posts every Sunday, and they have become an important aspect of our relationship.

Using the Greatest Expression, I became a better person, better son, better lacrosse player, better partner, friend, and student. I fully believe it will make me a better doctor. I look forward to teaching it to my patients.

Thank you for teaching me the tools to change me and my life."

A woman from Joplin, MO. wrote,

"Your Becoming the Greatest Expression of You saved my marriage."

I asked my blog readers how they benefited from the **Greatest Expression of You** process. I am filled with gratitude with the responses.

This woman gave me permission to share her letter but asked that I not disclose her name.

"I saw one of your Becoming the Greatest Expression of You posts on Facebook almost two years ago. What I read intrigued me, so I subscribed to your daily blog posts. I especially look forward to a new Greatest Expression post each Sunday.

At that point in time, my husband and I had been married just over seven years. Our relationship was struggling. We loved each other, but we weren't very nice to one another.

I felt ignored by him, and he thought that all I did was nag him. The truth is that the more ignored I felt, the more I nagged him. And the more I nagged, the more he ignored me. We argued more than we showed our love.

I used lipstick to write on my bathroom mirror the greatest expression of me. At that time, it was simple but powerful. I wrote, "I am happy, loving, and kind." My husband gave me *the eye* but didn't comment.

Each morning I meditated on being happy, loving, and kind. I memorized the joy I felt when we were dating, on our wedding day, and during that first year of marriage. I mentally rehearsed being happy, loving, and kind with my husband and in other areas of my life.

I again mentally rehearsed being happy, loving, and kind before greeting him when we came home from work.

Unknowingly, in the past I had been mentally rehearsing feeling ignored and hurt, to the point that when I saw him, I was already angry and picked a fight.

Those first few days, we didn't know how to be with each other. My husband was cautious around me and kept waiting for me to lash out at him.

We were both surprised by how quickly our relationship changed. He responded to my loving kindness with love and kindness. We laughed together, held hands, and made love like we were on our honeymoon.

Out of curiosity, my husband began reading your Greatest Expression of You blog posts, and I soon saw a sticky note on his bathroom mirror.

Thanks to this process, we are happily married. We are best friends, and we treat each other with love and kindness. Had we not changed, I think that we would have been divorced by now.

Your process saved my marriage! Thank you."

Clients who put this practice to use have experienced astounding results. People who use the **Greatest Expression of You** are changing. They are overcoming stress, anxiety, depression, chronic pain, and other health issues. The excitement I see in the eyes of someone who no longer has the symptoms of an autoimmune disease confirms the power of this process.

When you show up and be your best so that you are living in integrity with love, compassion, and joy, **you change**. You are happier, and because you are happier, the people around you are happier too.

Pope Francis said, "Rivers do not drink their own water; trees do not eat their own fruit; the sun does not shine on itself, and flowers do not spread their fragrance for themselves. Living for others is a rule of nature. We are all born to help each other. No matter how difficult it is . . . Life is good when you are happy, but much better when others are happy because of you."

The *Greatest Expression of You* is all about change. It is about transition. It is all about unlearning certain traits that we have memorized and relearning new states. It is about being purposeful in creating your future to be greater than your past.

Of course, the hardest part is not making the same old habitual choices again. How many times each day do you repeat the same old behaviors, thoughts, and emotional experiences you have lived by for years?

Does this old script serve you today? Is it getting you what you want? Or are you just continuing to relive the past? Is who you are becoming based on who you used to be?

The *Greatest Expression of You* is your opportunity to live a whole new script based on now. You get to break the habit of your old self and reinvent a new self. You purposefully choose to no longer think, act, or feel in predictable ways. You memorize new emotional states and let go of the old emotional states that no longer serve you. Another client was sharing with me the changes that she was making in her life, and she said that you "do it by choice."

"The universe is change; our life is what our thoughts make it."

Even though this maxim sounds like something you would hear in my office today, Marcus Aurelius (121–180) said it long ago. Change can be scary, but you can use your thoughts to move through the fear with excitement and joy. And the more you live in excitement and joy, the less room there is in your life for fear.

I know about the fear of change. In early 2017, my wife and I decided it was time to make a major change in our lives. We chose to move from one phase of our lives to another. We chose to sell our beautiful home on Bainbridge Island, Washington, and move to the desert in Coachella Valley. At the time of this decision, I had no idea as to the depth of transformation I would experience.

I left my large yard filled with rhododendrons, azaleas, clematis, echinacea, daisies, Japanese maples, Korean dogwoods, 200-foot-tall cedar trees, and abundant wildlife to a small desert yard of gravel.

I left behind family in Seattle and many dear Island friends and clients. I closed both my Seattle and Bainbridge Island offices, ended my twenty-three-year gym membership, and left the comfort and security of the "known." Throughout my life, I had never lived more than five years in any one house until Bainbridge.

Another component of this move was the transition from full productivity to a new phase with an eye on retirement, which encompasses a whole other level of mental and emotional gymnastics, learning to live life as a senior citizen.

As I continue processing this transition, I have been thinking about the definitions of change and transition. How are they different?

Merriam-Webster defines *change* as a transitive verb as "To make different" and as an intransitive verb as "To become different," "To undergo transformation." [27]

Webster defines *transition* as 1) a: passage from one state, stage, subject, or place to another: change b: a movement, development, or evolution from one form, stage, or style to another and 2) a: a musical modulation b: a musical passage leading from one section of a piece to another. "Transition."[28]

When I read these definitions, I was drawn immediately to "musical modulation—a musical passage leading from one section of a piece to another." I like to think of this transition as a musical modulation—a passage leading from one phase of my life to another.

The transformative change we chose to make was in part about reduction—downsizing. However, change is also about growth. Change is about mental, emotional, and spiritual expansion. It's like growing older—you are growing!

Over these past months, there have certainly been times when I resisted change. Times when I acted as less than my Best Self. In some of these moments, I was aware that I did not even want to be my Best Self! When I did allow myself to experience what I was thinking and feeling, I was eventually able to use ***The Greatest Expression of You*** process and find equanimity.

While there certainly have been some discordant notes along the way, I hope that one day I will look back on this move and find the harmony in this modulation in the symphony of my life.

---

[27] "Change." *Merriam-Webster.com Dictionary*, *Merriam-Webster*, https://www.merriam-webster.com/dictionary/change Accessed 9 Jan. 2021.
[28] "Transition." *Merriam-Webster.com Dictionary*, *Merriam-Webster*, https://www.merriam-webster.com/dictionary/transition. Accessed 9 Jan. 2021.

Becoming Whole

The Greatest Expression of You process is all about becoming whole. When you are being your Best Self, physical, mental, emotional, and spiritual healing happens. While you may not experience a "cure," you can experience healing.

This concept of healing without a cure was poignantly pointed out to me by a client who was nearing the end of her life. She knew she only had a few weeks to live, and she was determined to make the most of it by being her Best Self.

She talked extensively about Gratitude. I was particularly touched when she expressed her gratitude for her body's ability to heal. Even though she was dying from cancer, when she cut her finger, it healed. For this, she was grateful.

We cannot change the fact that each of us will die, but we can have some control over how we live. Live your life being the Greatest Expression of You—it is who you truly are.

I shared this story with a client, and she responded that she "couldn't imagine" being her Best Self and living with gratitude while dying from cancer. I smiled and told her that during the Christmas holidays my wife and I watched old Christmas movies. I have seen *Miracle on 34th Street* many times in my life, but this time there were two scenes that really caught my attention. One, was when Kris Kringle and Susan were talking and Kringle asked, "Do you know what the imagination is, Susan?"

The child nodded sagely. "That's when you see things that aren't really there."

"Well, not exactly," said Kris Kringle with a smile. "No -- to me, the imagination is a place all by itself. A very wonderful country. You've heard of the British Nation and the French Nation?"

Susan nodded again.

"Well, this is the Imagine Nation. And once you get there, you can do almost anything you want."

At another point in the movie, Kris Kringle said, "Christmas isn't just a day. It's a frame of mind." [29]

When you are being your Best Self, you really can do almost anything you want. Being the Greatest Expression of You is not just a process: it's a frame of mind. It's all about your *beingness.* It is about your attitude in life. It is about how you show up in your life. Show up in your life *being* your Best Self with gratitude and with giving thanks.

You have the plan all laid out. It is up to you to follow it. Now go and create your future to be greater than your past. My hope and prayer for you is that you are excited by the person you see yourself becoming!

I would love to hear from you about how *Being the Greatest Expression of Yourself* has changed you and your life. Please send me an email to Roger@Hypnosishealthinfo.com and share your story. If it is okay for me to anonymously share your story, let me know—otherwise, I promise to keep it confidential.

Epilogue

As I was writing this last chapter, our Luna died peacefully on our living room floor with her head in my lap. Her 13½-year-old

[29] *Miracle on 34th Street*, Valentine Davies (1947)

body could no longer afford her the life she wanted and deserved to live, but she continued to give love to her last breath. My hope and my prayer are that each day for the rest of my life, I strive to be the guy she thinks that I am.

Free Resources

Greatest Expression of You Blog

http://hypnosishealthinfo.com/library/becoming-greatest-expression-posts/

Self-Hypnosis Links

Here is info on Light Switch: (Week 1)

https://hypnosishealthinfo.com/hypnosismyths/self-hypnosis/light-switch/

Listen to these 2 or 3 times throughout the week:

https://www.hypnosishealthinfo.com/wp-content/uploads/2012/11/04-Learing-the-Light-Switch-Technique.mp3

https://www.hypnosishealthinfo.com/wp-content/uploads/2012/11/05-Using-the-Light-Switch-Technique.mp3

https://www.hypnosishealthinfo.com/wp-content/uploads/2012/11/06-Practicing-the-Light-Switch-Technique.mp3

Here is info on Suggestions: (Week 2)

https://hypnosishealthinfo.com/hypnosismyths/self-hypnosis/written-suggestions/

and

https://hypnosishealthinfo.com/hypnosismyths/self-hypnosis/hypnosis-suggestions/

Listen to these 2 or 3 times throughout the week:

https://www.hypnosishealthinfo.com/wp-content/uploads/2012/11/07-Hypnotic-Suggestions-Imagery.mp3

and

https://www.hypnosishealthinfo.com/wp-content/uploads/2012/11/08-Self-Hypnosis-Deepening.mp3

You can also find my hypnosis suggestions with images on Pinterest:
https://www.pinterest.com/hypnosishealth/boards/

Hypnosis Health Info Library

https://hypnosishealthinfo.com/library/

Medical Hypnosis

https://hypnosishealthinfo.com/medical-hypnosis/

Hypnosis Health Info Store

https://hypnosishealthinfo.com/store/

You Are Invited!

Roger Moore is available online worldwide.

I'm known for offering a safe, supportive environment where you feel heard and find hope. I teach you mindfulness-based tools that can lead you toward healing and growth.

Roger Moore
(760) 219-8079
Roger@HypnosisHealthInfo.com
www.HypnosisHealthInfo.com

Healthcare professionals across the U.S. and in several countries refer their patients to me.

Stay up to date with the latest news about ***Becoming the Greatest Expression of You*** by visiting:
www. GreatestExpressionBook.com

Made in the USA
Middletown, DE
24 May 2022